KU-472-771

PROPERTY OF
SMB

THE ILLUSTRATED BOOK OF

WORLD FABLES

THE ILLUSTRATED BOOK OF

WORLD FABLES

Collected by
Y Y COTTERELL

WINDWARD

First published 1979 by Windward
An imprint owned by W. H. Smith & Son Ltd.
Registered number 237811
Trading as WHS Distributors,
Euston Street,
Freemen's Common,
Aylestone Road,
Leicester LE2 7SS.

Produced by Guild Publishing
the Original Publications Division of
Book Club Associates

Designed by Leslie and Lorraine Gerry

Picture research by Celestine Dars

Set in 11/14pt Century Schoolbook and
printed by GPS (Print) Ltd., 142-170 Vauxhall St., SE11 5RT.

ISBN 0 7112 0020 3

CONTENTS

INTRODUCTION

Our modern view of fable has been not a little distorted by the Victorian emphasis on utility in children's literature. Fairy stories being placed beyond the pale, their appeal to the young person's imagination was considered not just suspect but the positive cause of moral depravity, there occurred a vogue for didactic fables which would 'do something to them!' The less cynical and more obvious of Aesop's fables found use as moral lessons on how to behave. *The Shepherd Boy Who Cried Wolf* was a favourite rebuke of the child who showed signs of restlessness or lack of resignation. The whole moral was underlined at the end in a tag – everything was exactly so. James Thurber (1894-1961) has delighted in playing with these tags at the end of his own pieces more recently. But at the same time, doubtless to the dismay of the Mr. Gradgrinds, the writing of literary fables was becoming, as Robert Louis Stevenson noted in 1874, 'a serious, if quite a miniature, division of creative literature'. In the review *On Lord Lytton's 'Fables in Song'* he wrote that the tendency in this contemporary form of writing was for 'the moral . . . to become more indeterminate and large' as 'the machinery employed to express it . . . becomes less and less fabulous'. Indeed, 'it ceases to be possible to append to it, in a tag, to the bottom of the piece, as one might write the name below a caricature; and the fable begins to rank with other forms of creative literature, as something too ambitious, in spite of its miniature dimensions, to be resumed in any succinct formula without loss of all that is deepest and most suggestive in it'.

This suggestiveness of other dimensions is the prime quality we find in Stevenson's own compositions as in many other of the fables included in this anthology. *The Two Matches* finds a fascinating parallel in the shorter Chinese story entitled *Love of Wine*. The reticence of both narratives, the absence of straightforward terms of reference, external yardsticks of right and wrong, leaves the reader to resolve for himself what may be meant. For this reason Stevenson had to admit the 'term Fable is not very easy to define'. Indeed, the form is a very old one. India, China and ancient West Asia, each had great collections of fabulous tales relating the actions of animals, men and gods. Such stories were a species of revelation. The mode of expression, the handling of the theme, communicates to something more innate than a literary sense. Something deeper. Fables seem to isolate the basic elements of life, giving at the same time a feeling of the unending continuity of human affairs. The persistent intrusion of humour, the irrepressible smile that must have greeted so many tales of apparently hopeless circumstances and futile endeavour, depends on affection and awe of the eccentricity in human character. It both humbles and exalts the individual at once.

The Touchstone is almost the epitome of fable, for the elder brother in his quest after the stone adopts a way of living which sets truth before security. The younger brother's mirror reflects only the deceiving image of life's surface, pleasing for those who would be self-deceived, whereas 'the clear pebble' brought back after so many trials by the elder brother gives access, like the detachment of wisdom, to the inner reality in which it can be perceived 'there is both good and bad'.

Jalal al-Din Rumi (1207-73) was conscious that his Persian stories drew upon a reservoir, an accumulated fund of human wisdom, when he claimed to be simply the medium of expression for the great thoughts of the ages. In China the Taoists also felt a sense of debt to the past: how could Lieh-tzu (450-380 BC) and Chuang-tzu (350-275 BC) do more than repeat the sayings of the 'Old Ones'? Their stories are closer to parables. It was the ineffable, that inward realm, that they were trying to chart. So the Buddha (563-479 BC) made a point by relating an episode in one of his previous births, as recorded in *The Jataka Tales*, and at the end of the nineteenth century Ramakrishna illustrated spiritual balance with the narrative of *The Holy Man And the Snake*.

From the Middle Ages come the stories entitled *The Man Who Had A Quarrelsome Wife* and *Covetousness and Envy*. These are *fabliaux*, very popular in France during the thirteenth century. Unlike the traditional fable and parable, the *fabliau* develops the story for its own sake. In this movement can be discerned a growing interest in human crotchets, as opposed to categorical sins, and the emergence of the personality of the writer. Jean Bodel (1170-1210) did much to shape and make popular this form of composition. Story telling was of course a source of great pleasure during the period: Chaucer used this social habit as the framework for *The Canterbury Tales*, where each evening one of the pilgrims relates a good story for the company's entertainment. By the time of Poggio Bracciolini (1380-1459), inhabitant of the Italian Renaissance, the need to speak wittily, to 'quip' and hold one's own in courtly and learned repartee, had engendered the *facetiae*. Here the success of the story depends solely on the humorous treatment of the subject. *A Very Short Sermon* is a choice example of quickwittedness: the monk's ready wit ensured that all the priests got to dinner on time and Poggio's invention permitted the telling of ecclesiastical backsliding in the Curia itself.

The modern fables contain echoes of such humour, though the end of Spike Milligan's hilarious *White Flag* is very much overshadowed by the nuclear mushroom. With the tales of T. F. Powys (1873-1953) and Franz Kafka (1883-1924) the form receives a conscious addition of symbol. Though Powys has more of the sensibility associated with the poet, both writers derive their power from the pursuit of ideas and sensations which inhabit the innermost recesses of the human mind. *A Little Fable* seems to telescope the entire predicament of twentieth-century man; its nervous intensity, macabre and final, is sufficient to set it apart from all the other animal tales.

This is not a comforting collection of moral tales. Fable was not the invention of Victorian suburbia. From time immemorial it has sought to provoke and vex the mind, always suggesting those other dimensions of life and death.

YONG YAP COTTERELL

ANIMALS AND BIRDS

THE MIGHTY FALLEN

WHEN a man loses the prestige that he once had, he becomes in his misfortune the plaything even of cowards.

A lion worn out with age and feebleness lay breathing his last. First came a boar and with a blow from its flashing tusks took revenge on him for an old injury. Then a bull lowered its horns and gored its enemy's body. An ass, seeing these attacks delivered with impunity, started kicking the lion's forehead with its heels. The lion was on the point of expiring. 'It was hard enough to bear,' he said, 'when those brave animals triumphed over me. But as for you, you shameful blot on creation, to be at your mercy as I die is like dying twice over.'

AESOP

THE WOLF AND HIS SHADOW

A WOLF, who was roaming about on the plain when the sun was getting low in the sky, was much impressed by the size of his shadow, and said to himself, 'I had no idea I was so big. Fancy my being afraid of a lion! Why, I, not he, ought to be King of the beasts'; and heedless of danger, he strutted about as if there could be no doubt at all about it. Just then a lion sprang upon him and began to devour him. 'Alas,' he cried, 'had I not lost sight of the facts, I shouldn't have been ruined by my fancies.'

AESOP

THE TOWN MOUSE AND THE COUNTRY MOUSE

A TOWN MOUSE and a Country Mouse were acquaintances, and the Country Mouse one day invited his friend to come and see him at his home in the fields. The Town Mouse came, and they sat down to a dinner of barleycorns and roots, the latter of which had a distinctly earthy flavour. The fare was not much to the taste of the guest, and presently he broke out with 'My poor dear friend, you live here no better than the ants. Now, you should just see how I fare! My larder is a regular horn of plenty. You must come and stay with me, and I promise you shall live on the fat of the land.' So when he returned to town he took the Country Mouse with him, and showed him into a larder containing flour and oatmeal and figs and honey and dates. The Country Mouse had never seen anything like it, and sat down to enjoy the luxuries his friend provided: but before they had well begun, the door of the larder opened and someone came in. The two mice scampered off and hid themselves in a narrow and exceedingly uncomfortable hole. Presently, when all was quiet, they ventured out again; but someone else came in, and off they scuttled again. This was too much for the visitor. 'Goodbye,' said he, 'I'm off. You live in the lap of luxury, I can see, but you are surrounded by dangers; whereas at home I can enjoy my simple dinner of roots and corn in peace.'

AESOP

THE FOX AND THE GRAPES

A HUNGRY fox saw some fine bunches of grapes hanging from a vine that was trained along a high trellis, and did his best to reach them by jumping as high as he could into the air. But it was all in vain, for they were just out of reach: so he gave up trying, and walked away with an air of dignity and unconcern, remarking, 'I thought those grapes were ripe, but I see now they are quite sour.'

AESOP

THE HARES AND FROGS

THE hares once gathered together and lamented the unhappiness of their lot, exposed as they were to dangers on all sides and lacking the strength and the courage to hold their own. Men, dogs, birds and beasts of prey were all their enemies, and killed and devoured them daily: and sooner than endure such persecution any longer, they one and all determined to end their miserable lives. Thus resolved and desperate, they rushed in a body towards a neighbouring pool, intending to drown themselves. On the bank were sitting a number of frogs, who, when they heard the noise of the hares as they ran, with one accord leaped into the water and hid themselves in the depths. Then one of the older hares who was wiser than the rest cried out to his companions, 'Stop, my friends, take heart; don't let us destroy ourselves after all: see, here are creatures who are afraid of us, and who must, therefore, be still more timid than ourselves.'

AESOP

THE FOX AND THE CROW

A CROW, perched in a tree with a piece of cheese in his beak, attracted the eye and nose of a fox. 'If you can sing as prettily as you sit,' said the fox, 'then you are the prettiest singer within my scent and sight.' The fox had read somewhere, and somewhere, and somewhere else, that praising the voice of a crow with a cheese in his beak would make him drop the cheese and sing. But this is not what happened to this particular crow in this particular case.

'They say you are sly and they say you are crazy,' said the crow, having carefully removed the cheese from his beak with the claws of one foot, 'but you must be near-sighted as well. Warblers wear gay hats and coloured jackets and bright vests, and they are a dollar a hundred. I wear black and I am unique.' He began nibbling the cheese, dropping not a crumb.

'I am sure you are,' said the fox, who was neither crazy nor nearsighted, but sly. 'I recognize you, now that I look more closely, as the most famed and talented of all birds, and I fain would hear you tell about yourself, but I am hungry and must go.'

'Tarry awhile,' said the crow quickly, 'and share my lunch with me.' Whereupon he tossed the cunning fox the lion's share of the cheese, and began to tell about himself. 'A ship that sails without a crow's nest sails to doom,' he said. 'Bars may come and bars may go, but crow bars last forever. I am the pioneer of flight, I am the map maker. Last, but never least, my flight is known to scientists and engineers, geometrists and scholars, as the shortest distance between two points. Any two points,' he concluded arrogantly.

'Oh, every two points, I am sure,' said the fox. 'And thank you for the lion's share of what I know you could not spare.' And with this he trotted away into the woods, his appetite appeased, leaving the hungry crow perched forlornly in the tree.

Moral: Twas true in Aesop's time, and La Fontaine's and now, no one else can praise thee quite as well as thou.

JAMES THURBER

A LESSON FOR FOOLS

A CROW was sitting on a branch of a tree with a piece of cheese in her beak when a fox observed her and set his wits to work to discover some way of getting the cheese. Coming and standing under the tree he looked up and said, 'What a noble bird I see above me! Her beauty is without equal, the hue of her plumage exquisite. If only her voice is as sweet as her looks are fair, she ought without doubt to be Queen of the Birds.' The crow was hugely flattered by this, and just to show the fox that she could sing she gave a loud caw. Down came the cheese, of course, and the fox, snatching it up, said, 'You have a voice, madam, I see: what you want is wits.'

AESOP

KING BANYAN DEER

ONCE upon a time, when King Brahmadatta ruled at Benares, the Bodhisattva was born a deer. At his birth his coat was of a golden hue, his eyes shone like jewels and his horns had the shine of polished silver. Attended by five hundred followers, he dwelt in the forest under the name of King Banyan Deer, not far from another golden deer also with a herd of five hundred followers, who was named Branch Deer.

In those days the king of Benares was passionately fond of hunting and always had meat at every meal. Every day he mustered the whole of his subjects, townsfolk and countryfolk alike, to the detriment of their business, and went hunting. The people became tired of this daily duty and worked out a plan. They sowed in the royal park grass for the deer to eat, dug water holes and made a fenced enclosure with a wide gate. Then in a body they went to the forest armed with sticks and all manner of weapons to find the deer. Surrounding the forest, they encircled both the haunt of Banyan and Branch deer; beating the ground and the bushes furiously they drove the deer from the trees and into the enclosure, fastening the gate firmly afterwards. A message was sent to King Brahmadatta to inform him that in future he could hunt at leisure in his own park.

Delighted by this arrangement the King granted immunity to the two golden deer only. Sometimes he would go and shoot a deer to bring back to the palace; sometimes his cook would go and shoot one. At first sight of the bow, the deer would dash off trembling for their lives, but after receiving two or three wounds they grew weary and faint and were slain. Banyan said to Branch:

'Friend, the deer are being destroyed in great numbers; and, though they cannot escape death, at least let them not be needlessly wounded. Let the deer go to the block by turns, one day one from my herd, and next day one from yours – the deer on whom the lot falls to go to the place of execution and lie down with its head on the block. In this way the other will escape stray arrows.'

This being agreed the deer went to the block by turns. Now one day the lot fell on a pregnant doe of the herd of Branch, and she went to Branch and said, 'Lord, I am with young. When I have brought forth my little one, there will be two of us to take our turn. Order me to be passed over this turn.' 'No, I cannot make your turn another's, he said; 'you must bear the consequences of your own fortune. Go!' Finding no favour with him, the doe approached the Bodhisattva and told her story. And he answered, 'Very well; you go away, and I will see that another takes your place.' To the block he went himself.

When the cook saw the golden neck of King Banyan Deer on the execution place, he rushed off to tell King Brahmadatta. The court came at once.

'My friend, king of the deer,' Brahmadatta asked, 'did I not promise you your life?'

Banyan deer told him of the doe's plight and the king said:

'My lord, the golden king of the deer, never yet saw I, even among men, one so abounding in charity, love and pity as you. I'm moved. Arise! I spare the lives of both you and her.'

'Though two be spared,' said Banyan, 'what shall the rest do, O king of men?'

'I spare them too.'

'And the deer outside your enclosure, what of them?'

'Their lives I spare too.'

'Deer are safe, but the other animals, are they?'

'Yes, I spare them too.'

'Animals need not fear now, but what about birds in the air and fish in water?'

'I spare them too, great lord,' King Brahmadatta said.

So King Banyan Deer by his willingness to face the block taught compassion for other creatures – whether with hoof, fin or wing.

JATAKA TALE

THE DOG IN THE MANGER

A DOG was lying in a manger on the hay which had been put there for the cattle, and when they came and tried to eat, he growled and snapped at them and wouldn't let them get at their food. 'What a selfish beast,' said one of them to his companions; 'he can't eat himself and yet he won't let those eat who can.'

AESOP

LOOK BEFORE YOU LEAP

A FOX fell into a well and was unable to get out again. By and by a thirsty goat came by, and seeing the fox in the well asked him if the water was good. 'Good?' said the fox, 'it's the best water I ever tasted in all my life. Come down and try it yourself.' The goat thought of nothing but the prospect of quenching his thirst, and jumped in at once. When he had had enough to drink, he looked about, like the fox, for some way of getting out, but could find none. Presently the fox said, 'I have an idea. You stand on your hind legs, and plant your forelegs firmly against the side of the well, and then I'll climb on to your back, and, from there, by stepping on your horns, I can get out. And when I'm out, I'll help you out too.' The goat did as he was requested, and the fox climbed on to his back and so out of the well; and then he coolly walked away. The goat called loudly after him and reminded him of his promise to help him out: but the fox merely turned and said, 'If you had as much sense in your head as you have hair in your beard you wouldn't have got into the well without making certain that you could get out again.'

AESOP

THE LION, THE FOX, AND THE STAG

A LION lay sick in his den, unable to provide himself with food. So he said to his friend the fox, who came to ask how he did, 'My good friend, I wish you would go to yonder wood and beguile the big stag who lives there, to come to my den: I have a fancy to make my dinner off a stag's heart and brains.' The fox went to the wood and found the stag and said to him, 'My dear sir, you're in luck. You know the lion, our King: well, he's at the point of death, and has appointed you his successor to rule over the beasts. I hope you won't forget that I was the first to bring you the good news. And now I must be going back to him; and, if you take my advice, you'll come too and be with him at the last.' The stag was highly flattered, and followed the fox to the lion's den, suspecting nothing. No sooner had he got inside that the lion sprang upon him, but he misjudged his spring, and the stag got away with only his ears torn, and returned as fast as he could to the shelter of the wood. The fox was much mortified, and the lion, too, was dreadfully disappointed, for he was getting very hungry in spite of his illness. So he begged the fox to have another try at coaxing the stag to his den. 'It'll be almost impossible this time,' said the fox, 'but I'll try'; and off he went to the wood a second time, and found the stag resting and trying to recover from his fright. As soon as he saw the fox he cried, 'You scoundrel, what do you mean by trying to lure me to my death like that? Take yourself off, or I'll do you to death with my horns.' But the fox was entirely shameless. 'What a coward you were,' said he; 'surely you didn't think the lion meant any harm? Why, he was only going to whisper some royal secrets into your ear when you went off like a scared rabbit. You have rather disgusted him, and I'm not sure he won't make the wolf King instead, unless you come back at once and show you've got some spirit. I promise you he won't hurt you, and I will be your faithful servant.' The stag was foolish enough to be persuaded to return, and this time the lion made no mistake, but overpowered him, and feasted right royally upon his carcase. The fox, meanwhile, watched his chance and, when the lion wasn't looking, filched away the brains to reward him for his trouble. Presently the lion began searching for them, of course without success: and the fox, who was watching him, said, 'I don't think it's much use your looking for the brains: a creature who twice walked into a lion's den can't have got any.'

AESOP

THE LIONESS AND THE VIXEN

A LIONESS and a vixen were talking together about their young, as mothers will, and saying how healthy and well-grown they were, and what beautiful coats they had, and how they were the image of their parents. 'My litter of cubs is a joy to see,' said the fox; and then she added, rather maliciously, 'But I notice you never have more than one.' 'No,' said the Lioness grimly, 'but that one's a lion.'
Quality, not quantity.

AESOP

THE HOLYMAN AND THE SNAKE

IN a meadow, where some cowherds looked after their cattle, there lived a poisonous snake. Everyone feared it and kept on the watch for it. One day, a holy man was seen, walking along the path through the meadow. The cowherd boys ran to him and said, 'Holy sir, please don't go that way! A poisonous snake lives over there.'

The holyman answered, 'My sons, let it be there if it must – I am not afraid of it, for I know a secret spell which will subdue it.' So saying, the holy man continued on his way; but none of the cowherd boys dared to follow him. And now the snake appeared, moving towards him with its hood spread. But, as it drew near, the holy man uttered his spell and it fell down at his feet as helpless as an earthworm.

Then the holy man said to it, 'Why do you go about doing harm to others? I am going to give you a mantra. As you repeat God's holy name, you will be set free from all desire to harm others; you will learn devotion to God and you will end by seeing him.' Having said this, the holy man whispered the holy name to the snake. And the snake, having been thus initiated, bowed down before its guru and asked, 'What disciplines shall I practise, holy sir?' The guru replied, 'repeat the holy name and do no harm to anyone.' Then, as he was about to leave, he said, 'I shall come back here again.'

As the days passed, the cowherd boys discovered that the snake would no longer bite anyone. So they pelted it with stones, but the snake didn't get angry; it behaved like an earthworm. One day, one of the boys grabbed it by the tail, whirled it around and dashed it against the ground. The snake vomited blood and lay on the ground unconscious. It showed no sign of life and the boys left it, thinking it was dead.

But, in the middle of the night, the snake revived and slowly dragged itself with the greatest difficulty to its hole. Its body was crushed. It could hardly move. Many days passed. The snake was a mere skeleton. It used to come out once every night, in search for food. During the day, it did not come out, for fear of the boys. Since it had received its initiation and the holy name of God, it had never hurt anyone. It kept alive by eating leaves and fruit that had fallen on the ground.

About a year later, the holy man came along that path again and at once asked about the snake. The cowherd boys told him it was dead. But the holy man could not believe this; for he knew that the snake could not die until the holy word he had given it at its initiation had borne fruit in the vision of God. So he looked for it, calling it by the name he had conferred on it. Hearing the voice of its guru, the snake came out of its hole and bowed down in deep devotion. 'How are you?' the holy man asked. 'I am well, sir,' the snake replied. 'Then why do you look so thin?' asked the holy man. And the snake answered, 'Master, you ordered me not to hurt any living creature, so I have been living on leaves and fruit only. Perhaps that's why I look thin.' For the snake had developed such purity of heart that it could not harbour any malice; and so it had almost forgotten how the cowherd boys had half killed it. 'You couldn't be in such a state just because of your diet,' said the holy man. 'There must be some other reason. Try to remember what it is.' Then the snake remembered how the cowherd boys had dashed it against the ground; and it said, 'Yes, Master, I remember now. One day, these cowherd boys dashed me against the ground. It is only their ignorance, for how could they know that my heart had been changed? How could they know that I wouldn't bite any more or harm anyone?' 'For shame!' said the holy man. 'Are you such a fool that you don't know how to protect yourself? I told you not to bite. I didn't tell you not to hiss. Why couldn't you have scared them away by hissing?'

SRI RAMAKRISHNA

NEGOTIATING FROM WEAKNESS

WHEN the hares addressed a public meeting and claimed that all should have fair shares, the lions answered: 'A good speech, Hairy-Feet, but it lacks claws and teeth such as we have.'

AESOP

THE LION AND THE BOAR

ONE hot and thirsty day in the height of summer a lion and a boar came down to a little spring at the same moment to drink. In a trice they were quarrelling as to who should drink first. The quarrel soon became a fight and they attacked one another with the utmost fury. Presently, stopping for a moment to take breath, they saw some vultures seated on a rock above evidently waiting for one of them to be killed, when they would fly down and feed upon the carcase. The sight sobered them at once, and they made up their quarrel, saying, 'We had much better be friends than fight and be eaten by vultures.'

AESOP

AS GOOD AS HIS WORD

A MOUSE ran over the body of a sleeping lion. Waking up, the lion seized it and was minded to eat it. But when the mouse begged to be released, promising to repay him if he would spare it, he laughed and let it go. Not long afterwards its gratitude was the means of saving his life. Being captured by hunters, he was tied by a rope to a tree. The mouse heard his groans, and running to the spot freed him by gnawing through the rope. 'You laughed at me the other day,' it said, 'because you did not expect me to repay your kindness. Now you see that even mice are grateful.'

A change of fortune can make the strongest man need a weaker man's help.

AESOP

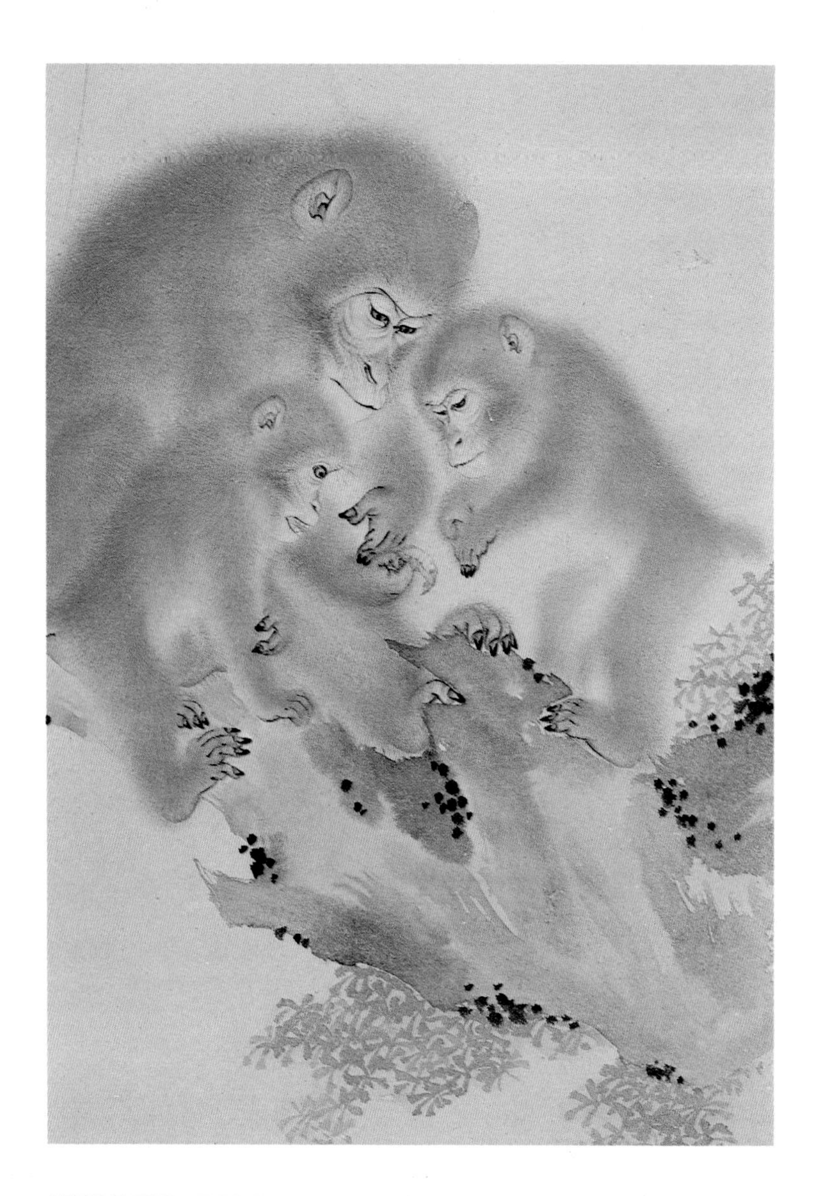

KILLED BY KINDNESS

IT is said that apes produce twins, on one of which they lavish affection, feeding it with great care, while they turn against the other and neglect it. But by a curious dispensation of providence, the one that the mother delights to care for and strains tightly to her breast is smothered to death, while the rejected one reaches maturity.

No forethought can prevail against destiny.

AESOP

ONE GOOD TURN DESERVES ANOTHER

A THIRSTY ant which had crawled into a rivulet was carried away by the current. A dove, seeing it in danger of drowning, broke off a twig and threw it into the water. The ant got onto it and was saved. Later, a fowler came with his limed sticks placed in position to catch the dove. When the ant saw him it stung his foot, and the pain made him drop the sticks, which frightened the dove away.

AESOP

ANTS

SEVERAL ants were pulling a grain of rice with all their might and main. 'Now let's have a rest. I hear that human beings eat this rice we pull with such effort. They are said to put it into a bowl and eat millions and billions of them at one time. Human beings must be great huge creatures!' The other ants said stoutly, one and all, 'I don't believe it!'

JAPANESE FABLE

COMEDY

THE STRIKER AND THE STRICKEN

A CERTAIN man struck Zaid on the neck. Zaid rushed at him to join issue with him.

'I have a question to ask you,' said the assailant. 'Answer me first, and then hit me back. I struck the nape of your neck; there was a sound of a slap. Now I have a question to ask you in all sincerity. That sound of a slap – was it caused by my hand or by the nape of your neck, highly honoured sir?'

Zaid replied, 'Because of the pain I have not the leisure to stand and reflect on this matter impartially. Since you have no pain, you do the pondering!'

RUMI

ONE FOOL MAKES TWO

A CARPENTER made a gate, and by mistake put the bar outside. The owner of the house abused him, 'You blind fool, you!' The carpenter retorted, 'It's you who are blind!' The owner taken aback, asked how that could be. 'If you were not blind, you wouldn't have employed a carpenter like me!'

CHINESE FABLE

THE SQUEAKING CHAIR

JUST as a certain man began to entertain a visitor he let out a fart. This caused him such embarrassment that he tried to pretend that the noise really came from his chair. He rubbed his finger on the arm of the chair, making a squeak. The guest said, 'The first one was more like it.'

CHINESE FABLE

A MAN AND HIS POLE

THERE was once a man in the kingdom of Lee who tried to enter a castle gate holding a long bamboo pole. First he held it upright, but it caught at the top and bottom, and he couldn't get it in. Then he held it sideways, but couldn't pass through with it. While he was cudgelling his brains about it, a passerby said, 'I'm not exactly a genius, bit if I were you I'd cut it into two in the middle. Then you would get in the gate.'

CHINESE FABLE

GIRLS

SOME girls are talking together. 'Generally speaking an ugly woman marries a handsome man, and a handsome woman marries an ugly one.' One of the girls spoke up. 'I'm sure to marry an ugly man.'

JAPANESE FABLE

THE MAN AND HIS TWO SWEETHEARTS

A MAN of middle age, whose hair was turning grey, had two sweethearts, an old woman and a young one. The elder of the two didn't like having a lover who looked so much younger than herself; so, whenever he came to see her, she used to pull the dark hairs out of his head to make him look old. The younger, on the other hand, didn't like him to look so much older than herself, and took every opportunity of pulling out the grey hairs, to make him look young. Between them, they left not a hair in his head, and he became perfectly bald.

AESOP

SHOOTING THE TIGER

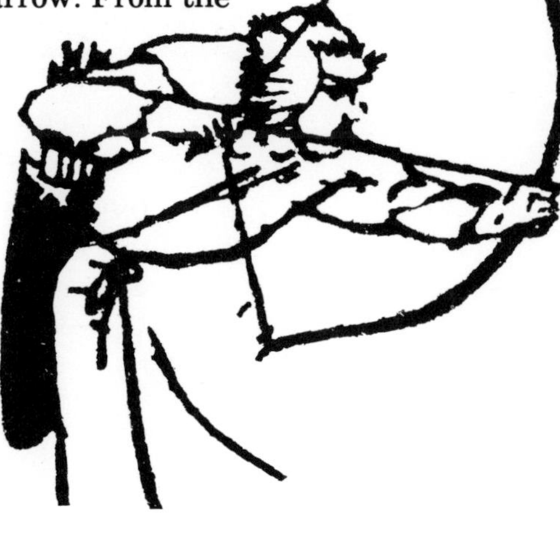

ONE man was carried away by a tiger. His son tried to shoot the tiger with a bow and arrow. From the tiger's mouth the father shouted:

'Aim at the legs. Don't spoil the hide!'

CHINESE FABLE

FORGETFULNESS

THREE men were sleeping in the same bed. The first man felt his thigh to be very itchy and, drugged by sleep, scratched vigorously the leg of the second man. Since the itching did not stop he scratched more strongly until blood came. The second man, finding the bed wet, thought the third man must have pissed and roused him. The third man got to the lavatory, adjacent to a brewery, and hearing the continuous dripping of wine, he thought it was himself, and stood there till daylight.

CHINESE FABLE

A LOVELY FIST

A CERTAIN man went to Peking, and when he came back he praised everything in Peking. One day he was walking in the moonlight with his father, and met someone who said, 'A fine moon tonight!' He answered, 'What's good about this moon? You should see the moon in Peking! It's far, far better.' His father was angry and said, 'The moon is the same everywhere. There's nothing specially good about the moon in Peking!' and clenching his fist he gave him a box of the ears. In a lachrymose voice the son replied, 'Your fist is nothing wonderful. You should feel the fists in Peking.'

CHINESE FABLE

DREAMING

ONE man dreamed that he went to the theatre and had just taken his seat, when his wife woke him up. Angry at this interruption he scolded her severely.

'Don't moan,' she advised. 'Hurry back! The play should have only just started.'

CHINESE FABLE

LIKE MAN, LIKE MONKEY

THERE was a lord who was extraordinarily thin and dark. He said to his attendant, 'I hear that people say I look like a monkey. Is it so?' The attendant replied deferentially, 'What an improper remark! I wonder who told your lordship such a thing. People only say that a monkey looks like your lordship.' Hearing this, the lord said, 'This is well said. That is as it should be,' and was not in the least indignant.

JAPANESE FABLE

THE THIEF

THE wife aroused her husband, and whispered, 'Dear, a thief has broken into the kitchen!' The husband jumped out of bed and seized him. But the thief was so strong that he grappled with the husband desperately for about an hour. In the end, the husband was stronger, and at last got the thief under his knee. He panted to his wife, 'Dear, give me a glass of water!' The thief from under him gasped out, 'And one for me too.'

JAPANESE FABLE

MAKING MEN

THE Jade Emperor, travelling in disguise, happened to stumble on a couple making love. When he inquired what they were doing, the lovers replied, 'Making men.'

'How many do you make in a year?' he asked next.

'One.'

'If this is so,' the Jade Emperor said, 'why should you need to be so busy?'

CHINESE FABLE

THE WOODCARVER AND THE PEASANTS

A FEW villagers from Aiello, a mountain hamlet in the Apennines, were sent to Arezzo to purchase a wooden crucifix that was to be installed in the church. They went to a carver who sold holy images, and when he realized that he was dealing with unusually uncouth and ignorant men, in order to get a good laugh at their expense, after he heard what they wanted, he asked them whether they wanted the Christ dead or alive. They took their time to take counsel; they discussed the whole thing among themselves in low voices and they concluded that they preferred him alive, for, if their fellow townsmen did not like him that way, they could always kill him!

POGGIO

TRAGEDY

THE GRAMMARIAN AND THE BOATMAN

A GRAMMARIAN once embarked in a boat. Turning to the boatman with a self-satisfied air he asked him:

'Have you ever studied grammar?'

'No,' replied the boatman.

'Then half your life has gone to waste,' the grammarian said.

The boatman thereupon felt very depressed, but he answered him nothing for the moment. Presently the wind tossed the boat into a whirlpool. The boatman shouted to the grammarian:

'Do you know how to swim?'

'No,' the grammarian replied, 'my well-spoken, handsome fellow.'

'In that case, grammarian,' the boatman remarked,

'the whole of your life has gone to waste, for the boat is sinking in these whirlpools.'

You may be the greatest scholar in the world in your time, but consider, my friend, how the world passes away – and time!

RUMI

THE YELLOW PAINT

IN a certain city there lived a physician who sold yellow paint. This was of so singular a virtue that whoso was bedaubed with it from head to heel was set free from the dangers of life, and the bondage of sin, and the fear of death for ever. So the physician said in his prospectus; and so said all the citizens in the city; and there was nothing more urgent in men's hearts than to be properly painted themselves, and nothing they took more delight in than to see others painted. There was in the same city a young man of a very good family but of a somewhat reckless life, who had reached the age of manhood, and would have nothing to say to the paint: 'To-morrow was soon enough,' said he; and when the morrow came he would still put it off. So he might have continued to do until his death; only, he had a friend of about his own age and much of his own manners; and this youth, taking a walk in the public street, with not one fleck of paint upon his body, was suddenly run down by a water-cart and cut off in the heyday of his nakedness. This shook the other to the soul; so that I never beheld a man more earnest to be painted; and on the very same evening, in the presence of all his family, to appropriate music, and himself weeping aloud, he received three complete coats and a touch of varnish on

the top. The physician (who was himself affected even to tears) protested he had never done a job so thorough.

Some two months afterwards, the young man was carried on a stretcher to the physician's house.

'What is the meaning of this?' he cried, as soon as the door was opened. 'I was to be set free from all the dangers of life; and here have I been run down by that self-same water-cart, and my leg is broken.'

'Dear me!' said the physician. 'This is very sad. But I perceive I must explain to you the action of my paint. A broken bone is a mighty small affair at the worst of it; and it belongs to a class of accident to which my paint is quite inapplicable. Sin, my dear young friend, sin is the sole calamity that a wise man should apprehend; it is against sin that I have fitted you out; and when you come to be tempted, you will give me news of my paint.'

'Oh!' said the young man, 'I did not understand that, and it seems rather disappointing. But I have no doubt all is for the best; and in the meanwhile, I shall be obliged to you if you will set my leg.'

'That is none of my business,' said the physician; 'but if your bearers will carry you round the corner to the surgeon's, I feel sure he will afford relief.'

Some three years later, the young man came running to the physician's house in a great perturbation. 'What is the meaning of this?' he cried. 'Here was I to be set free from the bondage of sin; and I have just committed forgery, arson and murder.'

'Dear me,' said the physician. 'This is very serious. Off with your clothes at once.' And as soon as the young man had stripped, he examined him from head to foot. 'No,' he cried with great relief, 'there is not a flake broken. Cheer up, my young friend, your paint is as good as new.'

'Good God!' cried the young man, 'and what then can be the use of it?'

'Why,' said the physician, 'I perceive I must explain to you the nature of the action of my paint. It does not exactly prevent sin; it extenuates instead the painful consequences. It is not so much for this world, as for the next; it is not against life; in short, it is against death that I have fitted you out. And when you come to die, you will give me news of my paint.'

'Oh!' cried the young man, 'I had not understood that, and it seems a little disappointing. But there is no doubt all is for the best: and in the meanwhile, I shall be obliged if you will help me to undo the evil I have brought on innocent persons.'

'That is none of my business,' said the physician; 'but if you will go round the corner to the police office, I feel sure it will afford you relief to give yourself up.'

Six weeks later, the physician was called to the town gaol.

'What is the meaning of this?' cried the young man. 'Here am I literally crusted with your paint; and I have broken my leg, and committed all the crimes in the calendar, and must be hanged to-morrow; and am in the meanwhile in a fear so extreme that I lack words to picture it.'

'Dear me,' said the physician. 'This is really amazing. Well, well; perhaps, if you had not been painted, you would have been more frightened still.'

R. L. STEVENSON

LOVE OF WINE

A BIBBER, dreaming that he was warming some excellent wine, woke up. He said regretfully, 'I should have drunk it cold.'

CHINESE FABLE

THE HUMAN BEING AND THE DINOSAUR

AGES ago in a wasteland of time and a wilderness of space, Man, in the upper case, and the dinosaur, in the lower, first came face to face. They stood like stones for a long while, wary and watchful, taking each other in. Something told the dinosaur that he beheld the coming glory and terror of the world, and in the still air of the young planet he seemed to catch the faint smell of his own inevitable doom.

'Greetings, stupid,' said Man. 'Behold in men the artfully articulated architect of the future, the chosen species, the certain survivor, the indestructible one, the monarch of all you survey, and of all that everyone else surveys, for that matter. On the other hand, you are, curiously enough, for all your size, a member of the inconsequent ephemera. You are one of God's moderately amusing experiments, a frail footnote to natural history, a contraption in a museum for future Man to marvel at, an excellent example of Jehovah's jejune juvenilia.'

The dinosaur sighed with a sound like thunder.

'Perpetuating your species,' Man continued, 'would be foolish and futile.'

'The missing link is not lost,' said the dinosaur sorrowfully. 'It's hiding.'

Man paid the doomed dinosaur no mind. 'If there were no Man it would be necessary to create one,' said Man, 'for God moves in mysterious, but inefficient, ways, and he needs help. Man will go on forever, but you will be one with the mammoth and the mastodon, for monstrosity is the behemother of extinction.'

'There are worse things than being extinct', said the dinosaur sourly, 'and one of them is being you.'

Man strutted a little pace and flexed his muscles. 'You cannot even commit murder,' he said, 'for murder requires a mind. You are capable only of dinosaurslaughter. You and you ilk are incapable of devising increasingly effective methods of destroying your own species and, at the same time, increasingly miraculous methods of keeping it extant. You will never live to know the two-party system, the multi-party system, and the one-party system. You will be gone long before I have made this the best of all possible worlds, no matter how possible all other worlds may be. In your highest state of evolution you could not develop the brain cells to prove innocent men guilty, even after their acquittal. You are all wrong in the crotch, and in the cranium, and in the cortex. But I have wasted enough time on you. I must use these fingers which God gave me, and now probably wishes He had kept for Himself, to begin writing those noble volumes about ME which will one day run to several hundred billion items, many of them about war, death, conquest, decline, fall, blood, sweat, tears, threats, warnings, boasts, hopelessness, hell, heels, and whores. There will be little enough about you and your ilk and your kith and your kin. Good and goodbye,' said Man in conclusion. 'I shall see to it that your species receives a decent burial, with some simple ceremony.'

Man, as it turned out, was right. The dinosaur and his ilk and his kith and his kin died not long after, still in lower case, but with a curious smile of satisfaction, or something of the sort, on the ephemeral faces.

Moral: The noblest study of mankind is Man, says Man.

THE SICK MAN AND THE FIREMAN

THERE was once a sick man in a burning house, to whom there entered a fireman.

'Do not save me,' said the sick man. 'Save those who are strong.'

'Will you kindly tell me why?' inquired the fireman, for he was a civil fellow.

'Nothing could possibly be fairer,' said the sick man. 'The strong should be preferred in all cases, because they are of more service in the world.'

The fireman pondered a while, for he was a man of some philosophy. 'Granted,' said he at last, as a part of the roof fell in; 'but for the sake of conversation, what would you lay down as the proper service of the strong?'

'Nothing can possibly be easier,' returned the sick man; 'the proper service of the strong is to help the weak.'

Again the fireman reflected, for there was nothing hasty about this excellent creature. 'I could forgive you being sick,' he said at last, as a portion of the wall fell out, 'but I cannot bear your being such a fool.' And with that he heaved up his fireman's axe, for he was eminently just, and clove the sick man to the bed.

R. L. STEVENSON

THE PENITENT

A MAN met a lad weeping. 'What do you weep for?' he asked.

'I am weeping for my sins,' said the lad.

'You must have little to do,' said the man.

The next day they met again. Once more the lad was weeping. 'Why do you weep now?' asked the man.

'I am weeping because I have nothing to eat,' said the lad.

'I thought it would come to that,' said the man.

R. L. STEVENSON

JUSTICE

THE FOOL'S JUDGMENT

A CERTAIN hungry porter found himself one day in the cook-shop district of the Petit Chatelet close enough to the savoury oven of a roast-meat seller to be able to hold his half-loaf of dry bread over the smoke that escaped from the said oven; with the result that it was richly flavoured and had a most royal taste. The wily cook let this go on without interference. But at the end when the last of this smoked bread had been bolted down, what does he do but seize the porter by the throat and in a threatening voice demand payment for the smoke of his meat. The outraged porter argued very plausibly that the meat in its roasting had come to no diminution, had lost nothing of its precious quality, and therefore that in nothing could he be regarded as a debtor. The smoke in question, he pointed out, would in

any case have evaporated in steam and been lost in the air; nor had he ever heard in all his days of roast-meat smoke being sold on the streets of Paris. The cook thereupon made answer haughtily that it wasn't his affair to feed hungry porters with the delicious smoke of expensive roast-meat and swore that if he didn't pay he'd switch his carrying pole off his shoulders. At this point the porter got his cudgel into play, turned up his sleeves and prepared to defend himself. The disturbance increased. The scandal-crazy Parisian crowd began gathering from every quarter. Then, at the most critical moment, who, by divine luck, should appear on the scene but Seigny John himself, the inspired Fool of that unequalled city. The moment he perceived him the cook cried out to the porter: 'Listen! Will you agree to trust this noble Seigny John to decide our quarrel?'

'By the face of God,' responded the porter, 'I surely will!'

Accordingly Seigny John, having made himself acquainted with every detail of the dispute, ordered the porter to produce from his wallet any kind of coin he chose. The porter did so and handed to him a King Philip penny. Seigny John took this penny and laid it on his left shoulder as if he were testing its proper and impressive weight. Then he tapped it on the palm of his left hand as if to assure himself that its excellent metal had no alloy. Then he laid it against the eyeball of his right eye as if to ascertain that it had been well minted. During all this time there was a deep hush and an expectant silence among that excited crowd; while the cook got more and more complacent and the porter more and more uneasy. At the end of it all and in the midst of a yet deeper silence Seigny John rang the coin several times on the top of the oven. Then, with the majestic air of a presidential judge, holding his bauble like a sceptre, wrapping his fool's cape of she-monkey-fur, with its paper ears all frizzed-out like organ-pipes, round his neck, and coughing magisterially two or three times, he announced his verdict in a resonant and solemn voice. 'The Court declares that the porter who has eaten his bread at the smoke of the roasted meat has civilly, duly, properly and correctly paid the owner of the said meat with the sound of his money. The said Court ordains that each party shall withdraw to his own particular place without cost and for a cause.' This verdict of the Fool of the City of Paris seemed so equitable and so admirable to the said doctors that they were driven to doubt whether if the case had been on trial before the Parliament of the said City or before the pontifical Rota of Rome, or even before the renowned, the classical, the immemorial court of the Areopagus at Athens, the sentence could have been delivered to the tune of such incredible justice. So consider, my friend, and consider again if you do not wish to take counsel of a fool.

FRANÇOIS RABELAIS

COVETOUSNESS AND ENVY

MY lords, having told many invented tales, I should like now to tell a true one. For the man who can tell only fables, that is to say, he cannot tell the truth as well as he can lie, is no true storyteller and is not worthy to serve at an important court; but the man who is proud of his trade rightfully should make one wise tale for every two vain ones.

Now it is certain truth that once, more than a hundred years ago, there were two friends who led a very bad life. For one was so full of envy that no one was more envious than he; and the other was so covetous that nothing could satisfy him. They were truly bad men and worse than bad: for covetousness leads to usury and makes men give short weight so they get greater riches; and envy is still worse, for it is a plague to everyone.

Now one day Covetousness and Envy rode out together, and, as I have been told, they came upon Saint Martin in an open field. And he had been in their company but a short while when he put them to the test to sound the ill will in their hearts. They came upon two well-travelled roads separated by a chapel, and there Saint Martin said to these men of evil life: 'My lords, at that church I shall turn off to the right, and I would leave you better off than when I met you. I am the worthy Saint Martin. If one of you will ask a gift of me, at once he shall have whatever he desires; and the one who keeps silent will immediately get twice as much as the other.'

Then the covetous one thought that he would allow his fellow to ask, and so he would get twice as much as he did, for he was greedy for the double gift. 'Dear companion,' he said, 'do you ask, and surely you will get whatever you ask for life. Let your wish be generous, for

if you know how to make the best of it you will be rich all your life.' But he whose heart was full of envy refused to make his wish, for he would have died of envy and sadness if the other got more than he did. So the two of them remained a great while without asking.

'What are you waiting for?' said the covetous one. 'Are you afraid it will turn out badly for you? I'll get twice as much as you do; you can't prevent it. Now ask! or I'll beat you worse than ever an ass was beaten crossing a bridge.'

'Sir,' the envious one answered, 'before you do me any harm, know that I will ask. But if I ask for money and wealth you will get twice as much as I. You will get nothing if I can help it.'

'Saint Martin,' he said, 'I ask that I may lose one of my eyes and my companion both of his. Thus he will be double afflicted.'

At once his eye was put out. The bargain was well kept: out of four eyes they lost three, and they gained nothing more besides. So Saint Martin made one of them one-eyed and the other blind, and by their own wish they lost. Bad luck, I say, to him who pities them, for they were of evil character.

JEAN BODEL

SOLOMON THE JUDGE

THEN came there two women, that were harlots, unto the king, and stood before him. And the one woman said, 'O my lord, I and this woman dwell in one house; and I was delivered of a child with her in the house. And it came to pass the third day after that I was delivered, that this woman delivered also: and we were together; there was no stranger with us in the house, save we two in the house. And this woman's child died in the night; because she overlaid it. And she arose at midnight, and took my son from beside me, while thine handmaid slept, and laid it in her bosom, and laid her dead child in my bosom. And when I rose in the morning to give my child suck, behold, it was dead: but when I had considered it in the morning, behold, it was not my son, which I did bear.' And the other woman said, 'Nay; but the living is my son, and the dead is thy son.' And this said, 'No; but the dead is thy son, and the living is my son.' Thus they spake before the king. Then said the king, 'The one saith, "This is my son that liveth, and thy son is the dead": and the other saith, "Nay; but thy son is the dead, and my son is the living".' And the king said, 'Bring me a sword.' And they brought a sword before the king. And the king said, 'Divide the living child in two, and give half to the one, and half to the other.' Then spake the woman whose the living child was unto the king, for her bowels yearned upon her son, and she said, 'O my lord, give her the living child, and in no wise slay it.' But the other said, 'Let it be neither mine nor thine, but divide it.' Then the king answered and said, 'Give her the living child, and in no wise slay it: she is the mother thereof.'

I KINGS 3

MANNERS

WHO FARTED?

A MAN and his wife were sitting in a room, when unknown to them a burglar broke in, and hid himself under the verandah. Late at night the wind made a sound at the back door, and the husband asked his wife, 'Did you fart?' 'Certainly not!' said his wife indignantly. She was so angry the husband was troubled and said, 'Oh well, perhaps a thief has broken in and is hiding somewhere, and *he* did it.' The thief came out from under the verandah and said, 'Now I must protest. . . .'

JAPANESE FABLE

THE COOK

WHILE a cook was carving meat at home he slipped a tender piece into his pocket. His wife saw this, and scolded him, saying: 'This is your home. Why do you do it?' The cook answered: 'I've forgotten.'

CHINESE FABLE

CONDOLENCES

A NOT very bright young man went with his uncle to pay a visit of condolence, his friend's father having died. Not knowing the proper behaviour on such an occasion he asked his uncle what to do, but the uncle, thinking it a nuisance to explain everything in detail, told him to do whatever he himself did. When they arrived at the gate of his friend's house, the uncle, being an unusually tall man, bumped his head on the gate as they went in. Seeing this his nephew, who was short of stature, went back a few paces, took a run, and jumped up and banged his own head on the gate. They went inside the house, and bowed to the mortuary tablet, but in doing so, by accident the uncle farted. The nephew tried to imitate him but could not, try as he would. At length he evacuated his bowels, whereupon the uncle took him home more in anger than in sorrow.

KOREAN FABLE

FAITH, HALF-FAITH, AND NO FAITH AT ALL

IN the ancient days there went three men upon pilgrimage; one was a priest, and one was a virtuous person, and the third was an old rover with his axe.

As they went, the priest spoke about the grounds of faith.

'We find the proofs of our religion in the works of nature,' said he, and beat his breast.

'That is true,' said the virtuous person.

'The peacock has a scrannel voice,' said the priest, 'as has been laid down always in our books. How cheering!'

he cried, in a voice like one that wept. 'How comforting!'

'I require no such proofs,' said the virtuous person.

'Then you have no reasonable faith,' said the priest.

'Great is the right, and shall prevail!' cried the virtuous person. 'There is loyalty in my soul; be sure, there is loyalty in the mind of Odin.'

'These are but playings upon words,' returned the priest. 'A sackful of such trash is nothing to the peacock.'

Just then they passed a country farm, where there was a peacock seated on a rail; and the bird opened its mouth and sang with the voice of a nightingale.

'Where are you now?' asked the virtuous person.

'And yet this shakes not me! Great is the truth, and shall prevail!'

'The devil fly away with that peacock!' said the priest; and he was downcast for a mile or two. But presently they came to a shrine, where a Fakeer performed miracles.

'Ah!' said the priest, 'here are the true grounds of faith. The peacock was but an adminicle. This is the base of our religion.' And he beat upon his breast, and groaned like one with colic.

'Now to me,' said the virtuous person, 'all this is as little to the purpose as the peacock. I believe because I see the right is greater and must prevail; and this Fakeer might carry on with his conjuring tricks till doomsday, and it would not play bluff upon a man like me.'

Now at this the Fakeer was so much incensed that his hand trembled; and, lo! in the midst of a miracle the cards fell from up his sleeve.

'Where are you now?' asked the virtuous person. 'And yet it shakes not me!'

'The devil fly away with the Fakeer!' cried the priest. 'I really do not see the good of going on with this pilgrimage.'

'Cheer up!' cried the virtuous person. 'Great is the right, and shall prevail!'

'If you are quite sure it will prevail,' says the priest.

'I pledge my word for that,' said the virtuous person.

So the other began to go on again with a better heart.

At last one came running, and told them all was lost: that the powers of darkness had besieged the Heavenly Mansions, that Odin was to die, and evil triumph.

'I have been grossly deceived,' cried the virtuous person.

'All is lost now,' said the priest.

'I wonder if it is too late to make it up with the devil?' said the virtuous person.

'Oh, I hope not,' said the priest. 'And at any rate we can but try. But what are you doing with your axe?' says he to the rover.

'I am off to die with Odin,' said the rover.

R. L. STEVENSON

WISDOM

CROCODILE TEARS

A MAN took some birds out of a cage and killed them by crushing their heads. While he was doing this, it so happened that tears began flowing from his eyes. The one of the birds in the cage said to the others:

'Take heart. I see that now he is weeping, and I am sure he will have mercy on us.'

The oldest bird replied: 'My son, do not look at his eyes, look at his hands.'

POGGIO

THE PROPHET

A PROPHET sat in the market-place and told the fortunes of all who cared to engage his services. Suddenly there came running up one who told him that his house had been broken into by thieves, and that they had made off with everything they could lay hands on. He was up in a moment, and rushed off, tearing his hair and calling down curses on the miscreants. The bystanders were much amused, and one of them said, 'Our friend professes to know what is going to happen to others, but it seems he's not clever enough to perceive what's in store for himself.'

AESOP

THE TWO SONS

A MAN had two sons. The elder left home while he was still young, and became a monk. Meanwhile, the younger got his education and became learned and virtuous. Then he married and settled down to fulfil his duties as a householder. After twelve years, the monk came to visit his brother, who was beside himself with joy. When they had eaten together, the younger brother asked the elder, 'Brother, you have given up our worldly pleasures and wandered around as a monk, all these years. Please tell me – what have you gained by it?' The elder brother said, 'You want to see what I've gained? Come with me!' So he took his brother to the bank of a neighbouring river, and he said, 'Watch!' and then he crossed the river, walking on the water, to the other bank; and he called back, 'Did you see that?' But the younger brother just paid half a penny to the ferryman, crossed the river by boat, went up to his brother and said, 'Didn't you see *me* cross the river by paying half a penny? Is that all you gained by twelve years of austerities?' Hearing his brother's words, the elder understood his mistake. And he now set his mind to realize God.

SRI RAMAKRISHNA

THE PRESCIENT GOLDSMITH

A CERTAIN man came to a goldsmith.

'Give me the scales,' he said, 'I want to weigh some gold.'

'Go away,' said the goldsmith. 'I do not have a sieve.'

'Give me the scales,' repeated the man. 'Have done with such jokes.'

'I do not have a broom in the shop,' said the goldsmith.

'Enough, enough!' said the man. 'No more of these jests. Give me the scales I am asking for. Do not make out you are deaf. Do not hop about in all directions.'

'I heard what you said,' said the goldsmith. 'I am not deaf. Do not get the idea that I am doddering. I heard all right. But you are a trembling old man. Your hand shakes, your body is not upright. That gold of yours moreover consists of the tiniest filings. Your hand shakes, and so the fragments of gold will spill. Then you will say, 'Master, bring me a broom, so that I may hunt for my gold in the dust! When you sweep up you will gather dust along with your gold, then you will say, 'I want a sieve, my hearty.' I saw the end completely from the beginning. Get out of here and go somewhere else, and good day to you!'

RUMI

WHAT A MAN NEEDS

IT used to be the custom in Mongolia that newly conquered land was given out by the king to his subjects by a rather strange method. A man was entitled to become the owner of as much land as he could ride round on horseback without stopping between sunrise and sunset.

Now it happened after one campaign that a certain man galloped off at the crack of dawn. He rode hard due north till nearly mid-day before he decided to change his direction to the east. Later afternoon saw him just turning south, and the evening shadows were long as the king and his court waited for the rider's return. Night was, in fact, almost upon them when a tiny figure was descried on the horizon. As it became larger they realised it was the man driving his mount furiously, racing against the setting sun. The watchers guessed that a very large area of land must have been enclosed and everyone was anxious to see if he would complete his claim in time.

He did at a moment before the sun went down, but the exhausted horse stumbled and threw the rider on his neck. With the dead man stretched at his feet the king shook his head and said to his courtiers:

'This man has won thousands of acres today and all he needs now is three by six.'

CHINESE FABLE

BOWING BEFORE THE STORM

A REED and an olive tree were disputing about their strength and their powers of quiet endurance. When the reed was reproached by the olive with being weak and easily bent by every wind, it answered not a word. Soon afterwards a strong wind began to blow. The reed, by letting itself be tossed about and bent by the gusts, weathered the storm without difficulty; but the olive, which resisted it, was broken by its violence.

The moral is that people should accept the situation in which they find themselves and yield to superior force. This is better than kicking against the pricks.

AESOP

KING SIVI

IN ancient India when the mighty King Sivi reigned in the city of Aritthapura, in the kingdom of Sivi, the Bodhisattva, was born as his son. They called him Prince Sivi.

The prince grew up and went to Taxila to study. When he returned he was so learned that his father made him viceroy of the kingdom. At his father's death he became king himself, and his rule was acclaimed for both its justice and goodness. He had six alms-halls built in the city, one at each of the four gates, one in the centre and one near the palace. Every day six hundred thousand pieces of money were distributed to the poor. On the eighth, fourteenth and fifteenth days of the month, the king never missed visiting the alms-halls to see that the poor received the money.

On a day of the full moon, he sat on the royal throne under the state umbrella, thinking of all that he had done for his people. He thought to himself:

'Of all outside objects, material things, there is nothing I have not given. But these kinds of gifts do not satisfy me. I want to give something which is a part of myself. Well, today, when I go the alms-hall, I swear that I will give whatever is asked of my person. Any part of my body will I give; the heart, a limb, the blood – let someone just name it. I am ready to put aside my crown and become another man's slave. Should any man request my eyes, he can even have them.'

Then he bathed himself with sixteen pitchers of perfumed water and put on his finest clothes. After a splendid meal, he mounted a richly decorated elephant and went to the alms-hall.

Sakka, king of the gods, saw everything and decided to test Sivi's resolution. He was curious to know whether or not the gift giving king would really sacrifice his eyes. So he disguised himself as an old, blind brahmin and took up a position outside the entrance of the alms-hall. When the king passed by, Sakka stretched out his hand and cried:

'Great king, there is no place in the world which does not echo with the fame of your good deeds. As you can see, I am blind. You have two eyes, I have none. A long way have I come to ask you for one of your eyes.'

When Sivi heard these words he was inwardly pleased. Had he not had just such a thought in the palace that morning? Here was the opportunity to fulfil his heart's desire, to give a gift that no man had ever given before.

'Who told you to come and request an eye?' the king asked. 'It is the most vital part of a man's body and difficult to part with.'

'It was no less than the king of the gods,' replied the

wizened brahmin. 'Sakka bade me to beg you for an eye, great king. Men say that to give an eye is the finest gift of all. Do not refuse me. Give me but one of your eyes.'

'One eye was requested,' said King Sivi, 'yet I will give you two.' Thereupon, the king and brahmin returned to the palace together.

Soon the whole city was a hubub of speculation. Everyone wondered that the king should wish to tear out his two eyes. Nobles and officials rushed to court; the queens, the army chief, leading ministers as well as other prominent courtiers entreated the king to revoke his promise. The begged him to load the brahmin with expensive gifts, such as gold, pearls, horses, elephants, chariots and whatever, but not to harm his own body for the sake of his faithful subjects.

'I have sworn to give anything that is asked of me,' King Sivi announced. 'An oath must not be broken. My soul will be in danger if I do so. Unasked, I would have given nothing. But the brahmin demands my eyes, and I must comply.'

'What do you want in return for your eyes?' the courtiers asked. 'What is your motive? Is it life, beauty, joy or strength? Why should the King of Siviland lose his eyes for the sake of the next world?'

'In giving my eyes,' the king told them, 'I do not seek glory, wealth, kingdoms, or many sons. I follow the example of holy men as my soul is full of joy at the thought of making gifts.'

The king turned to his surgeon and instructed him to remove his eyes. Although the surgeon hesitated and tried to persuade him against the decision, the king's will was obeyed at last. Immense pain struck Sivi, blood ran down his cheeks and spattered his rich clothes, but he endured the operation in silence. Sivi was quiet amid the cries of dismay uttered by the whole court.

'Here, brahmin,' King Sivi spoke after some time, 'take my eyes and place them in your sightless sockets. The eye of infinite knowledge is a thousand times dearer than this human eye. There is the reason for my action.'

The brahmin did as the king bid him. Then he left the palace and made his way out of the city under the amazed stares of the multitude; thence, Sakka was back with the gods.

Meanwhile Sivi, blind and unable to move about freely, decided to renounce his title and live as an ascetic in the royal park. He informed his ministers and sent for a chariot with one man to guide him. Against his wishes they carried him to the lakeside of the park in a golden litter and insisted on settling him comfortably there before going away.

On his throne in heaven Sakka watched uneasily till he determined to offer Sivi a boon – a chance to regain his eyesight. Quickly he was next to the blinded king, who asked who approached him.

'Sakka, king of the gods, has come to visit you from heaven. I am he and I wish to grant you a boon, royal sage. Name whatever you will.'

'O Sakka,' Sivi said, 'I have left wealth, strength, and treasure beyond count. I want death and nothing more, for I am blind.' 'King Sivi,' Sakka questioned, 'do you ask death because you are blind, or because you wish to die?'

'Because I am blind, my lord.'

'King Sivi, you made your gift thinking of the future. You were asked for a single eye, yet you gave a pair. Tell me the truth, and why you did so, and then only will your eyes be restored to you.'

'If you wish to return my eyes, Sakka, let them be restored as a consequence of my gift.'

'Though I am Sakka, king of the gods, I cannot give an

eye to anyone else. But on account of the supreme gift made by you and for no other reason, your eyes will come back.'

Joyfully the king said, 'Whatever man comes to me and asks for a gift, I will give it without question. If I speak the truth, let my eye appear.' As he uttered these words, one of his eyes reappeared in the empty socket. 'A brahmin came to me and begged for an eye,' Sivi continued. 'I gave both. That action afforded me the greatest joy. If I speak the truth, let my other eye appear.' Immediately the second eye did so.

These eyes are called the Eyes of Absolute and Perfect Truth.

After using his supernatural power to assemble the entire royal court in the park, Sakka thus addressed the king, 'Sivi, as a reward for your supreme act of self-sacrifice, I now present you with a pair of divine eyes. You will be able to see through rocks and walls, over hills and dales. A hundred miles on every side those eyes shall see.' With that Sakka took his leave of them and returned to heaven.

King Sivi went back to his palace thronged with his delighted subjects. As the crowds increased more and more Sivi decided to explain and extol his gift. Under a great pavilion by the palace gate he preached generosity and compassion.

'Now you have beheld these divine eyes,' he said, 'never eat food without giving something away. I received a divine eye in recompense for a mortal one. If you share things in your daily lives, my people, you will have heavenly rewards.'

On holy days King Sivi thus greeted his people, encouraging them to lead virtuous lives.

PHILOSOPHY

OMAR AND THE MAN WHO THOUGHT HE SAW THE NEW MOON

OMAR was caliph; the month of the fast had come round. A crowd of people ran to the top of a hill to draw a good omen from the sight of the crescent moon.

'See, Omar!' cried one. 'The new moon!'

Omar did not see any moon in the sky.

'This moon,' he remarked to the man, 'has risen from your imagination. Otherwise, how is it that I do not see the pure crescent, seeing that I am a better scanner of the skies than you? Wet your hand,' he went on, 'and rub it on your eyebrow, then take another look at the new moon.'

The man wetted his eyebrow, and no more saw the moon.

'The moon is no more, King!' he cried. 'It has vanished.'

'Yes,' commented Omar, 'The hair of your eyebrow became a bow and shot at you an arrow of surmise.'

One hair through becoming crooked had waylaid him completely, so that he falsely claimed boastfully to have seen the moon.

If one crooked hair can veil the whole sky, how will it be if all your parts are crooked?

RUMI

THE FOX AND THE HEDGEHOG

A FOX, in swimming across a rapid river, was swept away by the current and carried a long way downstream in spite of his struggles, until at last, bruised and exhausted, he managed to scramble on to dry ground from a backwater. As he lay there unable to move, a swarm of horseflies settled on him and sucked his blood undisturbed, for he was too weak even to shake them off. A hedgehog saw him, and asked if he should brush away the flies that were tormenting him; but the fox replied, 'Oh, please, no, not on any account, for these flies have sucked their fill and are taking very little from me now; but, if you drive them off, another swarm of hungry ones will come and suck all the blood I have left, and leave me without a drop in my veins.'

AESOP

THE ARCHER

SEVERAL men from Camerino one day were passing their time practising archery outside the city walls. A clumsy fellow shot an arrow and inflicted a slight wound on Prince Ridolfo, who was watching from a distance. The awkward archer was seized, and, believing that by doing so they would win the Prince's favour, everyone suggested an appropriate punishment for the offender. One of them proposed that his hand be cut off, so that he would no longer be able to shoot his bow. Ridolfo intervened and ordered that the man be released, saying that such a sentence would have been effective only if it had been carried out before he was hit.

POGGIO

THE SINKING SHIP

SIR,' said the first lieutenant, bursting into the Captain's cabin, 'the ship is going down.'

'Very well, Mr. Spoker,' said the Captain; 'but that is no reason for going about half-shaved. Exercise your mind a moment, Mr. Spoker, and you will see that to the philosophic eye there is nothing new in our position: the ship (if she is to go down at all) may be said to have been going down since she was launched.'

'She is settling fast,' said the first lieutenant, as he returned from shaving.

'Fast, Mr. Spoker?' asked the Captain. 'The expression is a strange one, for time (if you think of it) is only relative.'

'Sir,' said the lieutenant, 'I think it is scarcely worth while to embark in such a discussion when we shall all be in Davy Jones's Locker in ten minutes.'

'By parity of reasoning,' returned the Captain gently, 'it would never be worth while to begin any inquiry of importance; the odds are always overwhelming that we must die before we shall have brought it to an end. You have not considered, Mr. Spoker, the situation of man,' said the Captain, smiling, and shaking his head.

'I am much more engaged in considering the position of the ship,' said Mr. Spoker.

'Spoken like a good officer,' replied the Captain, laying his hand on the lieutenant's shoulder.

On deck they found the men had broken into the spirit room, and were fast getting drunk.

'My men,' said the Captain, 'there is no sense in this. The ship is going down, you will tell me, in ten minutes: well, and what then? To the philosophic eye, there is

nothing new in our position. All our lives long, we may have been about to break a blood-vessel or to be struck by lightning, not merely in ten minutes, but in ten seconds; and that has not prevented us from eating dinner, no, nor from putting money in the Savings Bank. I assure you, with my hand on my heart, I fail to comprehend your attitude.'

The men were already too far gone to pay much heed.

'This is a very painful sight, Mr. Spoker,' said the Captain.

'And yet to the philosophic eye, or whatever it is,' replied the first lieutenant, 'they may be said to have been getting drunk since they came aboard.'

'I do not know if you always follow my thought, Mr. Spoker,' returned the Captain gently. 'But let us proceed.'

In the powder magazine they found an old salt smoking his pipe.

'Good God,' cried the Captain, 'what are you about?'

'Well, sir,' said the old salt, apologetically, 'they told me as she were going down.'

'And suppose she were?' said the Captain. 'To the philosophic eye, there would be nothing new in our position. Life, my old shipmate, life, at any moment and in any view, is as dangerous as a sinking ship; and yet it is man's handsome fashion to carry umbrellas, to wear india-rubber over-shoes, to begin vast works, and to conduct himself in every way as if he might hope to be eternal. And for my own poor part I should despise the man who, even on board a sinking ship, should omit to take a pill or to wind up his watch. That, my friend, would not be the human attitude.'

'I beg pardon, sir,' said Mr. Spoker. 'But what is precisely the difference between shaving in a sinking ship and smoking in powder magazine?'

'Or doing anything at all in any conceivable circumstances?' cried the Captain. 'Perfectly conclusive; give me a cigar!'

Two minutes afterwards the ship blew up with a glorious detonation.

R. L. STEVENSON

A PHILOSOPHIC BALDPATE

A BALD man, who wore a wig, was riding one day, when a puff of wind blew the wig off, at which the bystanders guffawed. Reining in his horse, he said: 'It is not surprising that I cannot keep hair which is not mine on my head, since its proper owner, on whose head it grew, could not keep it there.' *Let no man be cast down by the accidents which befall him. What Nature did not give us at our birth can never be a permanent possession. Naked we came into the world, and naked shall we leave it.*

AESOP

WORTH

TZU Ch'i of Nan-poh was travelling on the Shang mountain when he saw a large tree which astonished him very much. A thousand chariot teams could have found shelter under its shade.

'What tree is this?' cried Tzu Ch'i. 'Surely it must have unusually fine timber.' Then looking up, he saw that its branches were too crooked for rafters; while as to the trunk he saw that its irregular grain made it valueless for coffins. He tasted a leaf, but it took the skin off his lips; and its odour was so strong that it would make a man as it were drunk for three days together.

'Ah!' cried Tzu Ch'i. 'This tree is good for nothing, and that is how it has attained this size. A wise man might well follow its example.'

CHUANG-TZU

FALLING DOWN

A MAN slipped and fell down. He got up and after a few steps, he fell down again. He said: 'If I had known, I would not have got up.'

CHINESE FABLE

TIME AND PLACE

LIEH-TZU exhibited his skill in archery to Poh Hun Wu Jen. Drawing his bow to its full, he placed a cup of water on his elbow and began to let fly. Hardly was one arrow out of sight ere another was on the string, the archer standing all the time like a statue.

'But this is shooting under ordinary conditions,' cried Poh Hun Wu Jen; 'it is not shooting under extraordinary conditions. Now I will ascend a high mountain with you, and stand on the edge of a precipice a thousand feet in height, and see how you can shoot then.'

Thereupon Wu Jen went with Lieh-Tzu up a high mountain, and stood on the edge of a precipice a thousand feet in height, approaching it backwards until one-fifth of his feet overhung the chasm, when he beckoned to Lieh-Tzu to come on. But the latter had fallen prostrate on the ground, with the sweat pouring down to his heels.

'The perfect man,' said Wu Jen, 'soars up to the blue sky, or dives down to the yellow springs, or flies to some extreme point of the compass, without change of countenance. But you are terrified, and your eyes are dazed. Your internal economy is defective.'

CHUANG-TZU

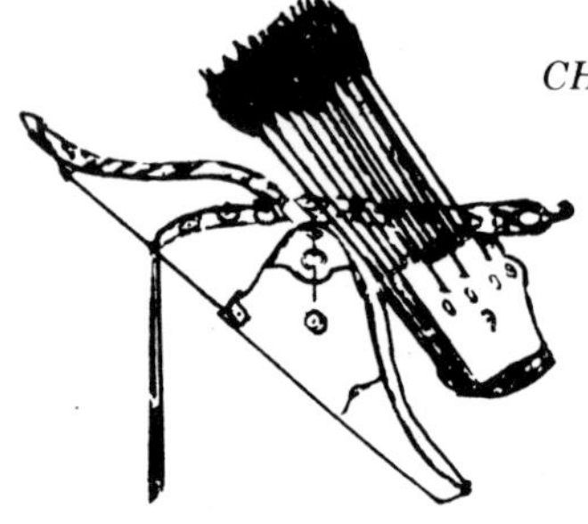

WIT

EASILY REMEDIED

THE rivers gathered together and made a complaint against the sea. 'Why,' they said, 'when we enter your waters fresh and fit to drink, do you make us salt and undrinkable?' Hearing itself thus blamed, the sea replied: 'Don't come: then you won't become salt.' *This fable satirizes people who make unreasonable accusations against those who are really their benefactors.*

AESOP

THE TADPOLE AND THE FROG

BE ashamed of yourself,' said the frog. 'When I was a tadpole, I had no tail.'

'Just what I thought!' said the tadpole. 'You never were a tadpole.'

R. L. STEVENSON

A VERY SHORT SERMON

IN the feast of St. Stephen, many people had flocked into one of our hill towns from numerous places. It was customary for a monk to deliver a public sermon. It was getting late, and as the priests were hungry, first one priest, then another, whispered into his ear to speak briefly. He ascended the pulpit and said:

'Brethren, last year I addressed you from this very place. I spoke of the sanctity of the life, and of the miracles of this Saint of ours, and I omitted nothing of what I had heard about him, or of what is written about him in the holy books; I am sure you remember all I said. Since that time, I haven't heard that he has done anything new; therefore, make the sign of the cross, and may the Lord bless you.'

THE WATCH-TOWER

A THIEF climbed up a watch-tower and was going to steal the bell there. The watchman woke up and challenged him. He pretended innocence and said, 'I want to ask you, how can I get to Honcho Street?' 'Ah, Honcho Street! You come down this ladder, and. . . .'

JAPANESE FABLE

OTHERS PLANTED FOR US

ANUSHIRVAN the Just, when riding through the countryside, saw an old man of eighty busily employed in planting walnut saplings. 'Old man', he said, 'you know that it will be years before those saplings bear fruit. Why do you waste so much effort on something that you can never share?' 'Sire,' replied the old man, 'others planted for us to eat, now we must plant for others to eat.' The king was pleased with this answer and gave the old man a hundred *ashrafis*. 'Sire,' said the old man, 'others planted for us to eat; we too planted for others to eat, but we did not die, and so we ourselves ate.' The king was even more pleased at this, and gave him another hundred *ashrafis*. 'Sire,' continued the old man, 'others planted for us to eat; we planted for others to eat, but we not only lived and ate ourselves, we even left something for our posterity to eat in comfort.' The king was delighted with this answer, and gave the man yet another hundred *ashrafis*. 'Sire,' began the old man – but at this juncture the king's chief minister, Bozorgmehr, interrupted. 'Let us leave, Your Majesty, for if we expose ourselves much longer to the ready wit of this astute old man, the royal treasury will soon be empty.'

PERSIAN FABLE

CHANGING HORSES

A MAN went out riding on an ass, and happened to meet a man on a horse. He dismounted suddenly, bowed, and said, 'Wouldn't you like to change your mount for mine?' The other said, 'Why, are you a fool?' 'No,' said the man, 'but I thought you might be.'

CHINESE FABLE

ADVICE TO A MAN WHO WAS CONCERNED OVER HIS DEBTS

A MAN from Perugia was walking down a street with a sad and worried look on his face. He ran into a fellow who asked him what the matter was. He replied that he had a lot of debts and that he couldn't possibly meet the payments. 'You blockhead,' said the other, 'mind your own business and let your creditors worry.'

POGGIO

FATE AND FORTUNE

THE DEAD RAT

MR. Yu was a wealthy man of the Liang State. His household was rolling in riches, and his hoards of money and silk and other valuables were quite incalculable. It was his custom to have banquets served, to the accompaniment of music, in a high upper hall overlooking the main road; there he and his friends would sit drinking their wine and amusing themselves with bouts of gambling.

One day, a party of young gallants happened to pass along the road. In the chamber above, play was going on as usual, and a lucky throw of the dice, which resulted in the capture of both fishes, evoked a loud burst of merriment from the players. Precisely at that moment, it happened that a kite which was sailing overhead dropped the carcass of a rat in the midst of the company outside. The young men held an angry consultation on the spot: 'This Mr. Yu,' they said 'has been enjoying his wealth for many a day, and has always treated his neighbours in the most arrogant spirit. And now, although we have never offended him, he insults us with this dead rat. If such an outrage goes unavenged, the world will look upon us as a set of poltroons. Let us summon up our utmost resolution, and combine with one accord to wipe him and his family out of existence!' The whole party signified their agreement, and when the evening of the day appointed had come, they collected, full armed for the attack, and exterminated every member of the family.

LIEH-TZU

SERVANT AND MASTER

MR. Yin of Chou was the owner of a large estate who harried his servants unmercifully, and gave them no rest from morning to night. There was one old servant in particular whose physical strength had quite left him, yet his master worked him all the harder. All day long he was groaning as he went about his work, and when night came he was reeling with fatigue and would sleep like a log. His spirit was then free to wander at will, and every night he dreamt that he was a king, enthroned in authority over the multitude, and controlling the affairs of the whole State. He took his pleasure in palaces and belvederes, following his own fancy in everything, and his happiness was beyond compare. But when he awoke, he was servant once more. To some one who condoled with him on his hard lot the old man replied: 'Human life may last a hundred years, and the whole of it is equally divided into nights and days. In the daytime I am only a slave, it is true, and my misery cannot be gainsaid. But by night I am a king, and my happiness is beyond compare. So what have I to grumble at?'

Now, Mr. Yin's mind was full of worldly cares, and he was always thinking with anxious solicitude about the affairs of his estate. Thus he was wearing out mind and body alike, and at night he also used to fall asleep utterly exhausted. Every night he dreamt that he was another man's servant, running about on menial business of every description, and subjected to every possible kind of abuse and ill-treatment. He would mutter and groan in his sleep, and obtained no relief until morning came. This state of things at last resulted in a serious illness, and Mr. Yin besought the advice of a friend. 'Your station in life,' his friend said, 'is a distinguished one, and you have wealth and property in abundance. In these respects you are far above the average. If at night you dream that you are a servant and exchange ease for affliction, that is only the proper balance in human destiny. What you want is that your dreams should be as pleasant as your waking moments. But that is beyond your power to compass.' On hearing what his friend said, Mr. Yin lightened his servant's toil, and allowed his own mental worry to abate; whereupon his malady began to decrease in proportion.

LIEH-TZU

THE TWO MATCHES

ONE day there was a traveller in the woods in California, in the dry season, when the Trades were blowing strong. He had ridden a long way, and he was tired and hungry, and dismounted from his horse to smoke a pipe. But when he felt in his pocket he found but two matches. He struck the first, and it would not light.

'Here is a pretty state of things!' said the traveller. 'Dying for a smoke; only one match left: and that certain to miss fire! Was there ever a creature so unfortunate? And yet,' thought the traveller, 'suppose I light this match, and smoke my pipe, and shake out the dottle here in the grass – the grass might catch on fire, for it is dry like tinder; and while I snatch out the flames in front, they might evade and run behind me, and seize upon yon bush of poison oak; before I could reach it, that would have blazed up; over the bush I see a pine tree hung with moss; that too would fly in fire upon the instant to its topmost bough; and the flame of that long torch – how would the trade wind take and brandish that through the inflammable forest! I hear this dell roar in a moment with the joint voice of wind and fire, I see myself gallop for my soul, and the flying conflagration chase and outflank me through the hills; I see this pleasant forest burn for days, and the cattle roasted, and the springs dried up, and the farmer ruined, and his children cast upon the world. What a world hangs upon the moment!' With that he struck the match, and it missed fire. 'Thank God!' said the traveller, and put his pipe in his pocket.

R. L. STEVENSON

A LITTLE FABLE

'ALAS,' said the mouse, 'the world is growing smaller every day. At the beginning it was so big that I was afraid, I kept running and running, and I was glad when at last I saw walls far away to the right and left, but these long walls have narrowed so quickly that I am in the last chamber already, and there in the corner stands the trap I must run into.' 'You only need to change your direction,' said the cat, and ate it up.

FRANZ KAFKA

CONFLICT

A REMARKABLE VICTORY

A LARGE and powerful army once set out to attack a small state in Southern China. But when the many companies of horsemen and footsoldiers reached the river which formed the border of the country they were going to invade there was a hesitation over making the crossing. News had arrived that the greatest general of the day was in command of the forces they would have to face.

However, across the river all that could be seen was an old tumbledown hut, perhaps built by a woodsman years before. So the army advanced and began to ford the river. Just as the first troops were halfway across a figure emerged from the hut and was immediately recognized to be the very general mentioned.

'It's a trap,' someone shouted at the front. 'Retreat, retreat!'

Those at the front turned and tried to go back as quickly as they could do so but those following were still pressing onwards unaware of the sudden danger. Soon panic was general and men and horses were swept away by the current as the army struggled against itself in the river. At last the soldiers fled as best they could to the shore they had so recently left and made off.

This remarkable victory, it was said afterwards, came from the ingenuity of two men. The famous general and his agent, the man who cried retreat. For the tiny state had hardly fifty men under arms at the time.

CHINESE FABLE

THE WHITE FLAG

THE two great Generals and the two great Armies faced each other across one great battlefield. The two great Generals marched about their two great Armies as they faced each other across one great battlefield. One great General said to himself, 'We can't hold out against this other great Army much longer,' and the other great General said, 'We can't hold out against this other great Army much longer,' so the first great General said to one of his great Sergeants, 'Hoist a white flag,' and the second great General said to his great Sergeant 'Hoist a white flag.'

Private Fred Lengths was commanded by one great General to haul up the flag. At the same time, Private Norrington Blitt had also been signalled by his General to hoist their white flag, and so the two great Armies stood surrendering to each other across the battlefield. It was very quiet, and the two flags were the only movement seen.

Three days passed, and one great General said 'What's happened?' as did the other great General. Both great Generals were informed that each side had surrendered to the other.

'Impossible,' said the first General.

'It can't be true,' said the second General.

'My arms are aching,' said Private Blitt, as did Private Lengths.

'How long have they had their flag up?' said the first great General.

'Three days,' at which time the second great General had asked the same question, and received the same answer.

'Tell them *we* surrendered *first*!'

KITCHNER
DID'NT WANT
ME.

The message was shouted across the great battlefield.

'No, no,' was the reply 'We surrendered first.' Neither side wanted to lose the initiative. Stalemate.

The two great Generals met in a tent in the middle of a field. 'According to my notes,' said the first, 'our flag went up at one minute to eleven on the 1st April.'

'So did ours', was the reply.

'But', said the first General, 'I gave the order to put the white flag up at a quarter to eleven . . .' and was met with the same reply. Stalemate II.

The first General screwed his eyes up, screwed his knees up, his nose, teeth and ears. 'Tell you what – my peace flag is whiter than yours.'

'Nonsense,' was the furious reply. 'Hold ours up to the light – not a stain in sight. We use the new Bluinite.'

'Bluinite!' guffawed the facing General. 'My dear fellow, Rinso, the new white Rinso, is my answer to you. That's why I say my flag is whiter.'

'The window test!' they said simultaneously.

In due course, a window was brought, against which the two flags were held. Alas, both were the same degree of white intensity. Stalemate III.

Meantime the makers of Bluinite and Rinso had heard of the conflict.

'You aren't going to let that lot get away with it,' said the Managing Director of Bluinite to the first General, at which time, as you can guess, Sir Jim Rinso was inciting the second General.

'I will prove who surrendered first,' he said, as the first great atomic blast exterminated them.

(Traditional)

SPIKE MILLIGAN

A COMPETITION OF WEAKNESS

THERE was a quarrel in a certain street. It got so violent that the bystanders said, 'Now then make it up! Beg each other's pardon!' One of them ran away and the other said, 'Damn him! He got away before I did!'

CHINESE FABLE

THE CITIZEN AND THE STRANGER

'LOOK around you,' said the citizen. 'This is the largest market in the world.'

'Oh, surely not,' said the traveller.

'Well, perhaps not the largest,' said the citizen, 'but much the best.'

'You are certainly wrong there,' said the traveller. 'I can tell you . . .'

They buried the stranger at the dusk.

R. L. STEVENSON

A CITY COAT OF ARMS

AT first all the arrangements for building the Tower of Babel were characterised by fairly good order, indeed the order was perhaps too perfect; too much thought was taken for guides, interpreters, accommodation for the workmen and roads of communication, as if there were centuries before one to do the work in. In fact the general opinion at that time was that one simply could not build too slowly; a very little insistence on this would have sufficed to make one hesitate to lay the foundations at all. People argued in this way: the essential thing in the whole business is the idea of building a tower that will reach to heaven. In comparison with that idea everthing else is secondary. The idea, once seized in its magnitude, can never vanish again; so long as there are men on the earth there will be also the irresistible desire to complete the building. That being so, however, one need have no anxiety about the future; on the contrary, human knowledge is increasing, the art of building has made progress and will make further progress, a piece of work which takes us a year may perhaps be done in half the time in another hundred years, and better done, too, more enduringly. So why exert oneself to the extreme limit of one's present powers? There would be some sense in doing that only if it were likely that the tower could be completed in one generation. But that is beyond all hope. It is far more likely that the next generation with their perfected knowledge will find the work of their predecessors bad, and tear down what has been built so as to begin anew. Such thoughts paralysed people's powers, and so they troubled less about the tower than the construction of a city for the workmen. Every nationality wanted the finest quarter for itself, and this gave rise to disputes, which developed into bloody conflicts. These conflicts never came to an end; to the leaders they were a new proof that, in the absence of the necessary unity, the building of the tower must be done very slowly, or indeed preferably postponed until universal peace was declared. But the time was spent not only in conflict; the town was embellished in the intervals, and this unfortunately enough evoked fresh envy and fresh conflict. In this fashion the age of the first generation passed away, but none of the succeeding ones showed any difference; except that technical skill increased and with it the occasion for conflict. To this must be added that the second and third generation recognised the senselessness of building a heaven-reaching tower; but by that time everyone was too deeply involved to leave the city. All the legends and songs that came to birth in that city are filled with longing for a prophesied day when the city would be destroyed by five successive blows from a gigantic fist. It is for that reason too that the city has a closed fist on its coat of arms.

FRANZ KAFKA

THE AXE

A MAN, having lost his axe, suspected his neighbour's son of having taken it. Certain peculiarities in his gait, his countenance and his speech, marked him out as the thief. In his actions, his movements, and in fact his whole demeanour, it was plainly written that he and no other had stolen the axe. By and by, however, while digging in a dell, the owner came across the missing implement. The next day, when he saw his neighbour's son again, he found no trace of guilt in his movements, his actions, or his general demeanour.

LIEH-TZU

MYSTERY

THE TOUCHSTONE

THE King was a man that stood well before the world; his smile was sweet as clover, but his soul withinsides was as little as a pea. He had two sons; and the younger son was a boy after his heart, but the elder was one whom he feared. It befell one morning that the drum sounded in the dun before it was yet day; and the King rode with his two sons, and a brave array behind them. They rode two hours, and came to the foot of a brown mountain that was very steep.

'Where do we ride?' said the elder son.

'Across this brown mountain,' said the King, and smiled to himself.

'My father knows what he is doing,' said the younger son.

And they rode two hours more, and came to the sides of a black river that was wondrous deep.

'And where do we ride?' asked the elder son.

'Over this black river,' said the King, and smiled to himself.

'My father knows what he is doing,' said the younger son.

And they rode all that day, and about the time of the sunsetting came to the side of a lake, where was a great dun.

'It is here we ride,' said the King; 'to a King's house, and a priest's, and a house where you will learn much.'

At the gates of the dun, the King who was a priest met them; and he was a grave man, and beside him stood his daughter, and she was as fair as the morn, and one that smiled and looked down.

'These are my two sons,' said the first King. 'And here is my daughter,' said the King who was a priest.

'She is a wonderful fine maid,' said the first King, 'and I like her manner of smiling.'

'They are wonderful well-grown lads,' said the second, 'and I like their gravity.'

And then the two Kings looked at each other, and said, 'The thing may come about.'

And in the meanwhile the two lads looked upon the maid, and the one grew pale and the other red; and the maid looked upon the ground smiling.

'Here is the maid that I shall marry,' said the elder. 'For I think she smiled upon me.'

But the younger plucked his father by the sleeve. 'Father,' said he, 'a word in your ear. If I find favour in your sight, might not I wed this maid, for I think she smiles upon me?'

'A word in yours,' said the King his father. 'Waiting is good hunting, and when the teeth are shut the tongue is at home.'

Now they were come into the dun, and feasted; and this was a great house, so that the lads were astonished; and the King that was a priest sat at the end of the board and was silent, so that the lads were filled with reverence; and the maid served them smiling with downcast eyes, so that their hearts were enlarged.

Before it was day, the elder son arose, and he found the maid at her weaving, for she was a diligent girl. 'Maid,' quoth he, 'I would faith marry you.'

'You must speak with my father,' said she, and she looked upon the ground smiling, and became like the rose.

'Her heart is with me,' said the elder son, and he went down to the lake and sang.

A little after came the younger son. 'Maid,' quoth he, 'if our fathers were agreed, I would like well to marry you.'

'You can speak to my father,' said she; and looked upon the ground, and smiled and grew like the rose.

'She is a dutiful daughter,' said the younger son, 'she will make an obedient wife.' And then he thought, 'What shall I do?' and he remembered the King her father was a priest; so he went into the temple, and sacrificed a weasel and a hare.

Presently the news got about; and the two lads and the first King were called into the presence of the King who was a priest, where he sat upon the high seat.

'Little I reck of gear,' said the King who was a priest, 'and little of power. For we live here among the shadow of things, and the heart is sick of seeing them. And we stay here in the wind like raiment drying, and the heart is weary of the wind. But one thing I love, and that is truth; and for one thing will I give my daughter, and that is the trial stone. For in the light of that stone the seeming goes, and the being shows, and all things besides are worthless. Therefore, lads, if ye would wed my daughter, out foot, and bring the stone of touch, for that is the price of her.'

'A word in your ear,' said the younger son to his father. 'I think we do very well without this stone.'

'A word in yours,' said the father. 'I am of your way of thinking; but when the teeth are shut the tongue is at home.' And he smiled to the King that was a priest.

But the elder son got to his feet, and called the King that was a priest by the name of father.

'For whether I marry the maid or no, I will call you by that word for the love of your wisdom; and even now I will ride forth and search the world for the stone of touch.'

So he said farewell, and rode into the world.

'I think I will go, too,' said the younger son, 'if I can have your leave. For my heart goes out to the maid.'

'You will ride home with me,' said his father.

So they rode home, and when they came to the dun, the King had his son into his treasury. 'Here,' said he, 'is the touchstone which shows truth; for there is no truth but plain truth; and if you will look in this, you will see yourself as you are.'

And the younger son looked in it, and saw his face as it were the face of a beardless youth, and he was well enough pleased; for the thing was a piece of a mirror.

'Here is no such great thing to make a work about,' said he; 'but if it will get me the maid I shall never complain. But what a fool is my brother to ride into the world, and the thing all the while at home!'

So they rode back to the other dun, and showed the mirror to the King that was a priest; and when he had looked in it, and seen himself like a King, and his house like a King's house, and all things like themselves, he

EAH

cried out and blessed God. 'For now I know,' said he, 'there is no truth but the plain truth; and I am a King indeed, although my heart misgave me.' And he pulled down his temple, and built a new one; and then the younger son was married to the maid.

In the meantime the elder son rode into the world to find the touchstone of the trial of truth; and whenever he came to a place of habitation, he would ask the men if they had heard of it. And in every place the men answered: 'Not only have we heard of it, but we alone, of all men, possess the thing itself, and it hangs in the side of our chimney to this day.' Then would the elder son be glad, and beg for a sight of it. And sometimes it would be a piece of mirror, that showed the seeming of things; and then he would say, 'This can never be, for at least there is the seeming.' And sometimes it would be a touchstone indeed, beautiful in hue, adorned with polishing, the light inhabiting its sides; and when he found this, he would beg the thing, and the persons of that place would give it him, for all men were very generous of that gift; so that at the last he had his wallet full of them, and they chinked together when he rode; and when he halted by the side of the way he would take them out and try them, till his head turned like the sails upon a windmill.

'A murrain upon this business!' said the elder son, 'for I perceive no end to it. Here I have the red, and here the blue and the green; and to me they seem all excellent, and yet shame each other. A murrain on the trade! If it were not for the King that is a priest and whom I have called my father, and if it were not for the fair maid of the dun that makes my mouth to sing and my heart enlarge, I would even tumble them all into the salt sea, and go home and be a King like other folk.'

But he was like the hunter that has seen a stag upon a mountain, so that the night may fall, and the fire be kindled, and the lights shine in his house; but desire of that stag is single in his bosom.

Now after many years the elder son came upon the sides of the salt sea; and it was night, and a savage place and the clamour of the sea was loud. There he was aware of a house, and a man that sat there by the light of a candle, for he had no fire. Now the elder son came in to him, and the man gave him water to drink, for he had no bread; and wagged his head when he was spoken to, for he had no words.

'Have you the touchstone of truth?' asked the elder son; and when the man had wagged his head, 'I might have known that,' cried the elder son. 'I have here a wallet full of them!' And with that he laughed, although his heart was weary.

And with that the man laughed too, and with the fuff of his laughter the candle went out.

'Sleep,' said the man, 'for now I think you have come far enough; and your quest is ended, and my candle is out.'

Now when the morning came, the man gave him a clear pebble in his hand, and it had no beauty and no colour; and the elder son looked upon it scornfully and shook his head; and he went away, for it seemed a small affair to him.

All that day he rode, and his mind was quiet, and the desire of the chase allayed. 'How if this poor pebble be the touchstone, after all?' said he: and he got down from his horse, and emptied forth his wallet by the side of the way. Now, in the light of each other, all the touchstones lost their hue and fire, and withered like stars at morning; but in the light of the pebble, their beauty remained, only the pebble was the most bright. And the elder son smote upon his brow. 'How if this be the truth?' he cried, 'that all are a little true?' And he took the pebble, and turned its light upon the heavens, and they deepened about him like the pit; and he turned it on the hills, and the hills were cold and rugged, but life ran in their sides so that his own life bounded; and he turned it on the dust and he beheld the dust with joy and terror; and he turned it on himself, and kneeled down and prayed.

'Now, thanks be to God,' said the elder son, 'I have found the touchstone; and now I may turn my reins, and ride home to the King and to the maid of the dun that makes my mouth to sing and my heart enlarge.'

Now when he came to the dun, he saw children playing by the gate where the King had met him in the old days; and this stayed his pleasure, for he thought in his heart, 'It is here my children should be playing.' And when he came into the hall, there was his brother on the high seat and the maid beside him; and at that his anger rose, for he thought in his heart. 'It is I that should be sitting there, and the maid beside me.'

'Who are you?' said his brother. 'And what make you in the dun?'

'I am your elder brother,' he replied. 'And I am come to marry the maid, for I have brought the touchstone of truth.'

Then the younger brother laughed aloud. 'Why,' said he, 'I found the touchstone years ago, and married the maid, and there are our children playing at the gate.

Now at this the elder brother grew as gray as the dawn. 'I pray you have dealt justly,' said he, 'for I perceive my life is lost.'

'Justly?' quoth the younger brother. 'It becomes you ill, that are a restless man and a runagate, to doubt my justice, or the King my father's, that are sedentary folk and known in the land.'

'Nay,' said the elder brother, 'you have all else, have

patience also; and suffer me to say the world is full of touchstones, and it appears not easily which is true.'

'I have no shame of mine,' said the younger brother. 'There it is, and look in it.'

So the elder brother look in the mirror, and he was sore amazed; for he was an old man, and his hair was white upon his head; and he sat down in the hall and wept aloud.

'Now,' said the younger brother, 'see what a fool's part you have played, that ran over all the world to seek what was lying in our father's treasury, and came back an old carle for the dogs to bark at, and without chick or child. And I that was dutiful and wise sit here crowned with virtues and pleasures, and happy in the light of my hearth.'

'Methinks you have a cruel tongue,' said the elder brother; and he pulled out the clear pebble and turned its light on his brother; and behold the man was lying, his soul was shrunk into the smallness of a pea, and his heart was a bag of little fears like scorpions, and love was dead in his bosom. And at that the elder brother cried out aloud, and turned the light of the pebble on the maid, and, lo! she was but a mask of a woman, and withinsides she was quite dead, and she smiled as a clock ticks, and knew not wherefore.

'Oh, well,' said the elder brother, 'I perceive there is both good and bad. So fare ye all as ye may in the dun; but I will go forth into the world with my pebble in my pocket.'

R. L. STEVENSON

THE SONG OF THE MORROW

THE King of Duntrine had a daughter when he was old, and she was the fairest King's daughter between two seas; her hair was like spun gold, and her eyes like pools in a river; and the King gave her a castle upon the sea beach, with a terrace, and a court of the hewn stone, and four towers at the four corners. Here she dwelt and grew up, and had no care for the morrow, and no power upon the hour, after the manner of simple men.

It befell that she walked one day by the beach of the sea, when it was autumn, and the wind blew from the place of rains; and upon the one hand of her the sea beat, and upon the other the dead leaves ran.

This was the loneliest beach between two seas, and strange things had been done there in the ancient ages. Now the King's daughter was aware of a crone that sat upon the beach. The sea foam ran to her feet, and the dead leaves swarmed about her back, and the rags blew about her face in the blowing of the wind.

'Now,' said the King's daughter, and she named a holy name, 'this is the most unhappy old crone between two seas.'

'Daughter of a King,' said the crone, 'you dwell in a stone house, and your hair is like the gold: but what is your profit? Life is not long, nor lives strong; and you live after the way of simple men, and have no thought for the morrow and no power upon the hour.'

'Thought for the morrow, that I have,' said the King's daughter; 'but power upon the hour, that have I not.' And she mused with herself.

Then the crone smote her lean hands one within the other, and laughed like a sea-gull. 'Home!' cried she. 'O daughter of a King, home to your stone house; for the longing is come upon you now, nor can you live any more after the manner of simple men. Home, and toil and suffer, till the gift come that will make you bare, and till the man come that will bring you care.'

The King's daughter made no more ado, but she turned about and went home to her house in silence. And when she was come into her chamber she called for her nurse.

'Nurse,' said the King' daughter, 'thought is come upon me for the morrow, so that I can live no more after the manner of simple men. Tell me what I must do that I may have power upon the hour.'

Then the nurse moaned like a snow wind. 'Alas!' said she, 'that this thing should be; but the thought is gone into your marrow, nor is there any cure against the thought. Be it so, then, even as you will; though power is less than weakness, power shall you have; and though the thought is colder than winter, yet shall you think it to an end.'

So the King's daughter sat in her vaulted chamber in the masoned house, and she thought upon the thought. Nine years she sat; and the sea beat upon the terrace, and the gulls cried about the turrets, and wind crooned in the chimneys of the house. Nine years she came not abroad, nor tasted the clean air, neither saw God's sky. Nine years she sat and looked neither to the right nor to the left, nor heard speech of any one, but thought upon the thought of the morrow. And her nurse fed her in silence, and she took of the food with her left hand, and ate it without grace.

Now when the nine years were out, it fell dusk in the autumn, and there came a sound in the wind like a sound of piping. At that the nurse lifted up her finger in the vaulted house.

'I hear a sound in the wind,' said she, 'that is like the sound of piping.'

'It is but a little sound,' said the King's daughter, 'But yet is it sound enough for me.'

So they went down in the dusk to the doors of the house, and along the beach of the sea. And the waves beat upon the one hand, and upon the other the dead leaves ran; and the clouds raced in the sky, and the gulls flew widdershins. And when they came to that part of

the beach where strange things had been done in the ancient ages, lo, there was the crone, and she was dancing widdershins.

'What makes you dance widdershins, old crone?' said the King's daughter; 'here upon the bleak beach, between the waves and the dead leaves?'

'I hear a sound in the wind that is like a sound of piping,' quoth she. 'And it is for that that I dance widdershins. For the gift comes that will make you bare, and the man comes that must bring you care. But for me the morrow is come that I have thought upon, and the hour of my power.'

'How comes it, crone,' said the King's daughter, 'that you waver like a rag, and pale like a dead leaf before my eyes?'

'Because the morrow has come that I have thought upon, and the hour of my power,' said the crone; and she fell on the beach, and, lo! she was but stalks of the sea tangle, and dust of the sea sand, and the sand lice hopped upon the place of her.

'This is the strangest thing that befell between two seas,' said the King's daughter of Duntrine.

But the nurse broke out and moaned like an autumn gale. 'I am weary of the wind,' quoth she; and she bewailed her day.

The King's daughter was aware of a man upon the beach; he went hooded so that none might perceive his face, and a pipe was underneath his arm. The sound of his pipe was like singing wasps, and like the wind that sings in windlestraw; and it took hold upon men's ears like the crying of gulls.

'Are you the comer?' quoth the King's daughter of Duntrine.

'I am the comer,' said he, 'and these are the pipes that a man may hear, and I have power upon the hour, and this is the song of the morrow.' And he piped the song of the morrow, and it was as long as years; and the nurse wept out aloud at the hearing of it.

'This is true,' said the King's daughter, 'that you pipe the song of the morrow; but that ye have power upon the hour, how may I know that? Show me a marvel here upon the beach, between the waves and the dead leaves.'

And the man said, 'Upon whom?'

'Here is my nurse,' quoth the King's daughter. 'She is weary of the wind. Show me a good marvel upon her.'

And lo! the nurse fell upon the beach as it were two handfuls of dead leaves, and the wind whirled them widdershins, and the sand lice hopped between.

'It is true,' said the King's daughter of Duntrine; 'you are the comer, and you have power upon the hour. Come with me to my stone house.'

So they went by the sea margin, and the man piped the song of the morrow, and the leaves followed behind them as they went. Then they sat down together; and the sea beat on the terrace, and the gulls cried about the towers, and the wind crooned in the chimneys of the house. Nine years they sat, and every year when it fell autumn, the man said, 'This is the hour, and I have power in it,' and the daughter of the King said, 'Nay, but pipe me the song of the morrow.' And he piped it, and it was long like years.

Now when the nine years were gone, the King's daughter of Duntrine got her to her feet, like one that remembers; and she looked about her in the masoned house; and all her servants were gone; only the man that piped sat upon the terrace with the hand upon his face; and as he piped the leaves ran about the terrace and the sea beat along the wall. Then she cried to him with a great voice, 'This is the hour, and let me see the power in it.' And with that the wind blew off the hood from the man's face, and, lo! there was no man there, only the clothes and the hood and the pipes tumbled one upon another in a corner of the terrace, and the dead leaves ran over them.

And the King's daughter of Duntrine got her to that part of the beach where strange things had been done in the ancient ages; and there she sat her down. The sea foam ran to her feet, and the veil blew about her face in the blowing of the wind. And when she lifted up her eyes, there was the daughter of a King come walking on the beach. Her hair was like the spun gold, and her eyes like pools in a river, and she had no thought for the morrow and no power upon the hour, after the manner of simple men.

R. L. STEVENSON

THE POOR THING

THERE was a man in the islands who fished for his bare bellyful and took his life in his hands to go forth upon the sea between four planks. But though he had much ado, he was merry of heart; and the gulls heard him laugh when the spray met him. And though he had little lore, he was sound of spirit; and when the fish came to his hook in the mid-waters, he blessed God without weighing. He was bitter poor in goods and bitter ugly of countenance, and he had no wife.

It fell at the time of the fishing that the man awoke in his house about the midst of the afternoon. The fire burned in the midst, and the smoke went up and the sun came down by the chimney. And the man was aware of the likeness of one that warmed his hands at the red peat fire.

'I greet you,' said the man, 'in the name of God.'

'I greet you,' said he that warmed his hands, 'but not in the name of God, for I am none of His; nor in the name of Hell, for I am not of Hell. For I am but a bloodless thing, less than wind and lighter than a sound, and the wind goes through me like a net, and I am broken by a sound and shaken by the cold.'

'Be plain with me,' said the man, 'and tell me your name and of your nature.'

'My name,' quoth the other, 'is not yet named, and my nature not yet sure. For I am part of a man; and I was a part of your fathers, and went out to fish and fight with them in the ancient days. But now is my turn not yet come; and I wait until you have a wife, and then shall I be in your son, and a brave part of him, rejoicing manfully to launch the boat into the surf, skilful to direct the helm, and a man of might where the ring closes and the blows are going.'

'This is a marvellous thing to hear,' said the man; 'and if you are indeed to be my son, I fear it will go ill with you; for I am bitter poor in goods and bitter ugly in face, and I shall never get me a wife if I live to the age of eagles.'

'All this have I come to remedy, my Father,' said the Poor Thing; 'for we must go this night to the little isle of sheep, where our fathers lie in the dead-cairn, and tomorrow to the Earl's Hall, and there shall you find a wife by my providing.'

So the man rose and put forth his boat at the time of the sunsetting; and the Poor Thing sat in the prow, and the spray blew through his bones like snow, and the wind whistled in his teeth, and the boat dipped not with the weight of him.

'I am fearful to see you, my son,' said the man. 'For methinks you are no thing of God.'

'It is only the wind that whistles in my teeth,' said the

Poor Thing, 'and there is no life in me to keep it out.'

So they came to the little isle of sheep, where the surf burst all about it in the midst of the sea, and it was all green with bracken, and all wet with dew, and the moon enlightened it. They ran the boat into a cove, and set foot to land; and the man came heavily behind among the rocks in the deepness of the bracken, but the Poor Thing went before him like a smoke in the light of the moon. So they came to the deadcairn, and they laid their ears to the stones; and the dead complained withinsides like a swarm of bees: 'Time was that marrow was in our bones, and strength in our sinews; and the thoughts of our head were clothed upon with acts and the words of men. But now are we broken in sunder, and the bonds of our bones are loosed, and our thoughts lie in the dust.'

Then said the Poor Thing: 'Charge them that they give you the virtue they withheld.'

And the man said: 'Bones of my fathers, greeting! for I am sprung of your loins. And now, behold, I break open the piled stones of your cairn, and I let in the noon between your ribs. Count it well done, for it was to be; and give me what I come seeking in the name of blood and in the name of God.'

And the spirits of the dead stirred in the cairn like ants; and they spoke: 'You have broken the roof of our cairn and let in the noon between our ribs; and you have the strength of the still-living. But what virtue have we? what power? or what jewel here in the dust with us, that any living man should covet or receive it? for we are less than nothing. But we tell you one thing, speaking with many voices like bees, that the way is plain before all like the grooves of launching. So forth into life and fear not, for so did we all in the ancient ages.' And their voices passed away like an eddy in a river.

'Now,' said the Poor Thing, 'they have told you a lesson, but make them give you a gift. Stoop your hand among the bones without drawback, and you shall find their treasure.'

So the man stooped his hand, and the dead laid hold upon it many and faint like ants; but he shook them off, and behold, what he brought up in his hand was the shoe of a horse, and it was rusty.

'It is a thing of no price,' quoth the man, 'for it is rusty.'

'We shall see that,' said the Poor Thing; 'for in my

thought it is a good thing to do what our fathers did, and to keep what they kept without question. And in my thought one thing is as good as another in this world; and a shoe of a horse will do.'

Now they got into their boat with the horse-shoe, and when the dawn was come they were aware of the smoke of the Earl's town and the bells of the Kirk that beat. So they set foot to shore; and the man went up to the market among the fishers over against the palace and the Kirk; and he was bitter poor and bitter ugly, and he had never a fish to sell, but only a shoe of a horse in his creel, and it rusty.

'Now,' said the Poor Thing,' 'do so and so, and you shall find a wife and I a mother.'

It befell that the Earl's daughter came forth to go into the Kirk upon her prayers; and when she saw the poor man stand in the market with only the shoe of a horse, and it rusty, it came in her mind it should be a thing of price.

'What is that?' quoth she.

'It is a shoe of a horse,' said the man.

'And what is the use of it?' quoth the Earl's daughter.

'It is for no use,' said the man.

'I may not believe that,' said she; 'else why should you carry it?'

'I do so,' said he, 'because it was so my fathers did in the ancient ages; and I have neither a better reason nor a worse.'

Now the Earl's daughter could not find it in her mind to believe him. 'Come,' quoth she, 'sell me this, for I am sure it is a thing of price.'

'Nay,' said the man, 'the thing is not for sale.'

'What!' cried the Earl's daughter. 'Then what make you here in the town's market, with the thing in your creel and nought beside?'

'I sit here,' says the man, 'to get me a wife.'

'There is no sense in any of these answers,' thought the Earl's daughter; 'and I could find it in my heart to weep.'

By came the Earl upon that; she called him and told him all. And when he had heard, he was of his daughter's mind that this should be a thing of virtue; and charged the man to set a price upon the thing, or else be hanged upon the gallows; and that was near at hand, so that the man could see it.

'The way of life is straight like the grooves of launching,' quoth the man. 'And if I am to be hanged let me be hanged.'

'Why!' cried the Earl, 'will you set your neck against a shoe of a horse, and it rusty?'

'In my thought,' said the man, 'one thing is as good as another in this world; and a shoe of a horse will do.'

'This can never be,' thought the Earl; and he stood and looked upon the man, and bit his beard.

And the man looked up at him and smiled. 'It was so my fathers did in the ancient ages,' quoth he to the Earl, 'and I have neither a better reason nor a worse.'

'There is no sense in any of this,' thought the Earl, 'and I must be growing old.' So he had his daughter on one side, and says he: 'Many suitors have you denied, my child. But here is a very strange matter that a man should cling so to a shoe of a horse, and it rusty; and that he should offer it like a thing on sale, and yet not sell it; and that he should sit there seeking a wife. If I come not to the bottom of this thing, I shall have no more pleasure in bread; and I can see no way, but either I should hang or you should marry him.'

'By my troth, but he is bitter ugly,' said the Earl's daughter. How if the gallows be so near at hand?'

'It was not so,' said the Earl, 'that my fathers did in the ancient ages. I am like the man, and can give you neither a better reason nor a worse. But do you, prithee, speak with him again.'

So the Earl's daughter spoke to the man. 'If you were not so bitter ugly,' quoth she, 'my father the Earl would have us marry.'

'Bitter ugly am I,' said the man, 'and you as fair as May. Bitter ugly I am, and what of that? It was so my fathers –'

'In the name of God,' said the Earl's daughter, 'let your fathers be!'

'If I had done that,' said the man, 'you had never been chaffering with me here in the market, nor your father the Earl watching with the end of his eye.'

'But come,' quoth the Earl's daughter, 'this is a very strange thing, that you would have me wed for a shoe of a horse, and it rusty.'

'In my thought,' quoth the man, 'one thing is as good –'

'Oh, spare me that,' said the Earl's daughter, 'and tell me why I should marry.'

'Listen and look,' said the man.

Now the wind blew through the Poor Thing like an infant crying, so that her heart was melted; and her eyes were unsealed, and she was aware of the thing as it were a babe unmothered, and she took it to her arms, and it melted in her arms like the air.

'Come,' said the man, 'behold a vision of our children, the busy hearth, and the white heads. And let that suffice, for it is all God offers.'

'I have no delight in it,' said she; but with that she sighed.

'The ways of life are straight like the grooves of launching,' said the man; and he took her by the hand.

'And what shall we do with the horseshoe?' quoth she.

'I will give it to your father,' said the man; 'and he can make a kirk and a mill of it for me.'

It came to pass in time that the Poor Thing was born; but memory of these matters slept within him, and he knew not that which he had done. But he was a part of the eldest son; rejoicing manfully to launch the boat into the surf, skilful to direct the helm, and a man of might where the ring closes and the blows are going.

R. L. STEVENSON

FAMILIES

THREE FOOLISH SISTERS

THERE once lived in a certain place three foolish sisters. The eldest, on the wedding night flatly refused to take off her clothes, so her husband, thinking she disliked him, went home the next morning, and never came again. Hearing this, the second sister, when she married, stripped herself of all her clothes, made a bundle of them, and walked into the room with it on her head the first night. The bridegroom got a shock, and went off immediately. The youngest sister, on her wedding night, stood outside the door and asked, 'Shall I come in with my clothes on, or off?' This bridegroom also thought she must be out of her mind, and would not stay!

KOREAN FABLE

THE UNICORN IN THE GARDEN

ONCE upon a sunny morning a man who sat in a breakfast nook looked up from his scrambled eggs to see a white unicorn with a gold horn quietly cropping the roses in the garden. The man went up to the bedroom where his wife was still asleep and woke her. 'There's a unicorn in the garden,' he said. 'Eating roses.' She opened one unfriendly eye and looked at him. 'The unicorn is a mythical beast,' she said, and turned her back on him. The man walked slowly downstairs and out into the garden. The unicorn was still there; he was now browsing among the tulips. 'Here, unicorn,' said the man, and he pulled up a lily and gave it to him. The unicorn ate it gravely. With a high heart, the man went upstairs and roused his wife again. 'The unicorn,' he said, 'ate a lily.' His wife sat up in bed and looked at him, coldly. 'You are a booby,' she said, 'and I am going to have you put in the booby-hatch.' The man, who had never liked the words 'booby' and 'booby-hatch,' and who liked them even less on a shining morning when there was a unicorn in the garden, thought for a moment. 'We'll see about that,' he said. He walked over to the door. 'He has a golden horn in the middle of his forehead,' he told her. Then he went back to the garden to watch the unicorn; but the unicorn had gone away. The man sat down among the roses and went to sleep.

As soon as the husband had gone out of the house, the wife got up and dressed as fast as she could. She was very excited and there was a gloat in her eye. She telephoned the police and she telephoned a psychiatrist; she told them to hurry to her house and bring a strait-jacket. When the police and the psychiatrist arrived they sat down and looked at her, with great interest. 'My husband,' she said, 'saw a unicorn this morning.' The

police looked at the psychiatrist and the psychiatrist looked at the police. 'He told me it ate a lily.' The psychiatrist looked at the police and the police looked at the psychiatrist. 'He told me it had a golden horn in the middle of its forehead.' At a solemn signal from the psychiatrist, the police leaped from their chairs and seized the wife. They had a hard time subduing her, for she put up a terrific struggle, but they finally subdued her. Just as they got her into the strait-jacket, the husband came back into the house.

'Did you tell your wife you saw a unicorn?' asked the police. 'Of course not,' said the husband. 'The unicorn is a mythical beast.' 'That's all I wanted to know,' said the psychiatrist. 'Take her away. I'm sorry, sir, but your wife is as crazy as a jay bird.' So they took her away, cursing and screaming, and shut her up in an institution. The husband lived happily ever after.

Moral: Don't count your boobies until they are hatched.

JAMES THURBER

THE MAN WHO HAD A QUARRELSOME WIFE

A PEASANT who married a very contrary-minded wife went for a walk with her one day in a pasture. The peasant remarked to his wife that he had never seen a pasture so evenly mowed. She quickly answered: 'No, it wasn't mowed, it was done with a sharp scissors.' The peasant said: 'On the contrary, it was mowed.' 'No,' said the woman, 'clipped.'

Then the peasant grew angry. 'It is clear you are a fool,' he said, 'this grass was cut with a scythe. But you've always got to get your word in. Now I intend that my word shall prevail, and I am stubborn enough to make it do so.' The peasant threw her down and cut out her tongue. Then he asked for her opinion: was the pasture mowed with a scythe or clipped with a scissors? Since she could not speak, she showed with her fingers that a scissors had cut it, and that no scythe had mown it.

By this tale I mean to show, as has been often proven, that when a fool speaks foolishness and someone comes along and speaks sense to him, the fool will not believe him but will grow angry; and, even when he knows he is wrong, he will try to make his lie prevail, which no one can do by remaining silent.

A REAL MAN

A CERTAIN man, beaten by his wife, hid under the bed. 'Come out!' screamed the wife. 'When a man says he won't come out,' he said, 'he won't!'

CHINESE FABLE

SHARING BOOTS

TWO brothers bought a pair of boots between them, but the older one wore them every day. In order to get his share the younger brother used to wait every evening for his older brother to go to sleep, then he would put on the boots and walk all over the place, till they were worn out.

'We ought to buy another pair,' the older brother suggested again. The younger brother did not agree and said, 'I can't afford the sleep.'

CHINESE FABLE

FATHER AND SON

THE father came back home intoxicated, and said to his son, 'Hey, Magoruku you've got three heads. I'm not going to leave my fine house to a monster like you!' The son, just as drunk, retorted, 'That's all right with me. Who'd want a house going round and round like this?'

JAPANESE FABLE

THE BRIDE

MRS. Cains stood at her cottage window watching. Exactly opposite the window was a large farmhouse, square and prosperous, with its drive gates set open.

Mrs. Cains watched more expectantly and more greedily.

A large furniture van entered the gates of the farmhouse and was soon beginning to unload. Out of the van were being taken heavy costly things such as a wealthy farmer with a mind as heavy as his purse would be likely to buy. Mrs. Cains watched what was being taken out of the van with an interested greed, but her daughter Laura who was standing near to her frowned, because she knew what her mother was thinking of.

' 'Tis a fine full house of furniture that 'eve a got together, that should move any young girl to go to 'e.'

Mrs. Cains shuffled her feet and turned meaningly to her daughter.

Laura stood pensive. She rarely smiled or spoke. She was a girl of strange ways, a splendid carnal creature, and eighteen years old that day.

Her magnificent body, that grew, so her mother fancied, always at night time, had gathered new beauties to it every dark hour since she was a tiny child, and now waited only for the wedding bells to ring.

'I'd give all the world,' said Mrs. Cains, 'to see into farmer's house, and' thee be big enough to go over to 'e, who be always asking for 'ee to come.'

Laura watched the unloading of the furniture, with her lips a little parted, and with eyes that were as full of the dark rage of love as the deepest seas.

'Though 'e be a hoarding miser farmer do buy,' said Mrs. Cains wishing to get a word from Laura, as to whether or no she would receive the attentions of the farmer and go and be kind to him.

' 'Tis the third load of fine things that 'e've a-had in to tempt 'ee, an' thee baint no little chick now to be afeared of a man.'

Laura frowned. Her frown was the first sign that she had been thinking at all about farmer Score, the rich widower, who had filled his house with costly furniture for her sake only.

Mrs. Cains shuffled her feet, she looked at the girl suggestively, as though she were weighing her exact worth for love – she wanted to, as a mother will want sometimes, to push her out to the man. . . .

Laura Cains had grown up in Little Dodder a flower amongst weeds. Her mother had never understood her silent ways. She had taken her to dances and fairs as soon as she was fourteen, but she never could get her to talk to a young man. Laura would only stand entirely silent and watch the people about her, as she watched farmer Score, who stood now in the open gateway; for the van had unloaded its goods and was gone.

' 'E did buy all for thee to notice,' exclaimed Mrs. Cains, looking invitingly at the farmer. ' 'E did ask I if me maid were as well grown as a heifer cow that be waiting ready for breeding. And I did tell 'e me Laura were just such a breeder for a strong man to have over to 's home. Do 'ee see how 'e do stand in road and do beckon, 'e be asking for 'ee to go over to farm.'

Mrs. Cains touched Laura, she wished to raise her desire for the man, so that she might at least want to be married.

'Oh, thee'd be nice to kiss an' cuddle,' she said, 'thee'd be nice for a strong man to hold in 's arms, thee'd be something for 'e to 'ave hold on.'

Mr. Score was holding out a hand like a crooked claw

and beckoning. His grey head and pale greedy face and heavy figure leaning forward, and formed exactly the kind of man that Mrs. Cains could admire. While behind him there was the large house and the furniture.

Laura watched him without any interest, exactly as she had watched two lovers embracing, one harvest time when the moon was full, and her mother and she were returning from a fair.

' 'E be a strong man to content a nice maid,' remarked Mrs. Cains.

Laura's firm full bosom responded to her breathing, without any flutter or hurry, as a child who sleeps well; she frowned.

Mr. Score walked over to the cottage, entered the room, and talked in a chatty manner about the furniture.

Laura turned a little and looked at him.

Mrs. Cains fancied that her daughter's colour heightened.

'Thee baint always been a farmer,' she said to Mr. Score.

'Thee were a Stonebridge butcher in past days?'

'Yes, yes,' replied the farmer, looking hungrily at the girl, 'there weren't no one that could strike down a cow same as I, an' I don't never mind having to strike twice.'

Mrs. Cains smiled approvingly, her daughter was grown deathly pale.

Laura went over to the farmer.

'Strike me down too if you want to,' she said. . . .

Upon her wedding day a great many envious eyes looked at Laura, and many a man wished himself in farmer Score's place who was to take her to his home that day.

The wedding was upon a Saturday afternoon, for the avaricious farmer couldn't bear to think of his men idling away their time in the fields while he was being married in church.

The only man in the church who dared not look at Laura was Mr. Crocket, the clergyman, who, fearing the awful presence near to him of so much loveliness, looked down at his square-toed boots in mute agony.

'I don't wish to get into any trouble with God about a woman,' thought Mr. Crocket, whose own eyes now compelled him to steal a glance at Laura as she kneeled, 'but I would give all that I have. . . .'

Mr. Score was churchwarden, and always carried the bag round during the last hymn. He liked to finger money, as well, or even better, than to fill his house with furniture for the sake of obtaining full possession of the body of a lovely girl.

Mrs. Cains saw him go to church as usual the day after the wedding, and as soon as he was out of the way she hoped Laura would beckon her to come over and view the wealth of her home. But instead of beckoning her to come, Laura walked over herself, came into the cottage room, and looked out of the window just as she had done when the furniture was being unloaded.

Her mother looked at her curiously.

' 'Tis nice to be married,' she said.

Laura's right hand held her own left hand idly in her lap, she stood entirely still and watched in utter detachment her new home.

' 'Tis nice to be married,' said her mother again.

Laura breathed quietly, and looked across the way.

'Let we go and see all they fine things?' whispered Mrs. Cains, feeling with her hand the warmth of Laura's bare arm.

Presently Mrs. Cains began to sniff; something, she thought, must be on fire. She hurried about her cottage but could find nothing burning.

She came to the window again where Laura was standing.

Laura smiled. She held up her left hand and looked at the wedding ring upon it, she folded her hands again and stood as before.

Mrs. Cains sniffed uneasily.

'Let we go,' she said, 'for I do want to see all they things.'

A white puff of smoke broke out from one of the upper windows at the farm that happened to be open – this was the wedding bedroom.

'Oh,' cried Mrs. Cains, 'house be on fire an' all they wonders will be burned.' Laura smiled again. In a few moments the whole house opposite was ablaze. . . .

When Mr. Score came from the church carrying the collection money, he found his house a mass of flames. He threw himself into the midst of them hoping to save something.

'I thought he would want to do that,' said Laura speaking to her mother for the first time that morning. . . .

Mr. Crocket was sorry when he heard that Farmer Score was burnt to death, because he feared that if he looked at Mrs. Score, who would be sure to attend the funeral, that it might be the worse for him. But he found his temptation easier to resist at the burial than at the wedding, because there was the grave to look into.

T. F. POWYS

HOW THINGS FALL DOWN

THE face of a henpecked husband was scratched by his wife. Next day at work his boss asked him about the wound. Embarrassed, the man invented a story about how during the previous evening he had been sitting under a vine trellis when it collapsed; hence, the scratch on his face. His boss found the explanation hard to believe and began to point out shortcomings in the account, when his own wife, who happened to be eavesdropping, rushed furiously into the room. Quickly he said to the henpecked husband, 'Please retire for a moment, for I fear my vine trellis is falling down too.'

CHINESE FABLE

LAST THINGS

ON HIS OWN FUNERAL

WHEN Chuang-Tzu was about to die, his disciples expressed a wish to give him a splendid funeral. But Chuang-Tzu said, 'With Heaven and Earth for my coffin and shell; with the sun, moon, and stars as my burial regalia; and with all creation to escort me to the grave, – are not my funeral paraphernalia ready to hand?'

'We fear,' argued the disciples, 'lest the carrion kite should eat the body of our Master,' to which Chuang-Tzu replied, 'Above ground I shall be food for kites; below I shall be food for molecrickets and ants. Why rob one to feed the other?'

CHUANG-TZU

THE MAN AND HIS FRIEND

A MAN quarrelled with his friend.

'I have been much deceived in you,' said the man.

And the friend made a face at him and went away.

A little after, they both died, and came together before the great white Justice of the Peace. It began to look black for the friend, but the man for a while had a clear character and was getting in good spirits.

'I find here some record of a quarrel,' said the justice, looking in his notes. 'Which of you was in the wrong?'

'He was,' said the man. 'He spoke ill of me behind my back.'

'Did he so?' said the justice. 'And pray how did he speak about your neighbours?'

'Oh, he had always a nasty tongue,' said the man.

'And you chose him for your friend?' cried the justice. 'My good fellow, we have no use here for fools.'

So the man was cast in the pit, and the friend laughed out aloud in the dark and remained to be tried on other charges.

R. L. STEVENSON

A MEAN MAN

A STINGY old man who was about to die made his last request, that they should not spend much money, and that they should send him to the temple before dawn for cheapness sake. The relatives gathered together, and said they couldn't do this and that. The old man sat up and said, 'Well, I won't die then!'

JAPANESE FABLE

THE TALKING SKULL

A HUNTER goes into the bush. He finds an old human skull. The hunter says: 'What brought you here?' The skull answers: 'Talking brought me here.' The hunter runs off. He runs to the king. He tells the king: 'I found a dry human skull in the bush. It asks you how its father and mother are.'

The king says: 'Never since my mother bore me have I heard that a dead skull can speak.' The king summons the Alkali, the Saba, and the Degi and asks them if they have ever heard the like. None of the wise men has heard the like and they decide to send a guard out with the hunter into the bush to find out if his story is true and, if so, to learn the reason for it. The guard accompany the hunter into the bush with the order to kill him on the spot should he have lied. The guard and the hunter come to the skull. The hunter addresses the skull: 'Skull, speak.' The skull is silent. The hunter asks as before: 'What brought you here?' The skull does not answer. The whole day long the hunter begs the skull to speak, but it does not answer. In the evening the guard tells the hunter to make the skull speak, and when he cannot they kill him in accordance with the king's command. When the guard are gone the skull opens its jaws and asks the dead hunter's head: 'What brought you here?' The dead hunter's head replies: 'Talking brought me here!'

AFRICAN FABLE

NO ROOM

THERE could be no doubt about it, that those who said, 'thik grave ground do belong to Mr. Truggin', were nearer to the truth of the matter, at least in the local idea, than the few austere ones who would still call the Tadnol Churchyard 'God's Acre'.

''Tain't no acre at all,' Mr. Truggin had once said in contradiction of the grander notion. ''Tis only two of they rods and three small poles.'

No one in Tadnol, not even Farmer Spenke's father, whose memory went back until it was near washed by the waters of the flood, had ever remembered any other sexton than Mr. Truggin.

Mr. Truggin, who was by no means wizened or ghoulish, but an old man of spirit whose cheeks were like Pride's pippins, trimmed the graves all the year round, with the same thought and care that a popular grocer bestows upon his shop windows at Christmas time.

And, indeed, Mr. Truggin by such care and tending, aided by the natural grace and friendliness of the place, gave to this final home such a comforting and pleasant look – outside at least – that no one, not even those who knew their days were numbered, could fail to think cheerfully and happily of the brown soil below, and the white snowdrops above, in Mr. Truggin's garden. If anyone had a welcome anywhere they found it there. Nowhere else the air blew so feelingly, and no tree's shade in summer was so heavy with love as the great yew's, and no moss flowered so finely in February as the moss that grew upon the churchyard wall.

If anyone in Tadnol wished to do anything from whence real happiness was sure to follow, 'to die' was the word; and next, 'to be buried by Mr. Truggin.'

As was proper and right, no person who understood such an important mystery as well as Mr. Truggin did, could take a lenient view of any interference in the arrangement of those grassy mounds. And when Mr. Dibben from Weyminster, with the long face and longer trousers of a curate at St. Luke's, came to do a month's duty at Tadnol, and told Mr. Truggin disrespectfully that dead bodies ought to be planted in rows like broad beans, the sexton sniffed with disapproval.

'At Weyminster,' said Mr. Dibben, 'they are all lined up like soldiers.'

'For folk do like to bide where they be known. They dead,' said the sexton, warming to the subject, 'be as particular as we. 'Twouldn't do for Miss Jarrett to be put next door to old Burt, who did fall into river twenty times before 'e drowned 'isself in en.'

Mr. Dibben looked at the grave mounds, and took from his pocket the chart of the churchyard, and held it out for

Mr. Truggin to see.

' 'Tis a pretty picture,' remarked the sexton, smiling.

'If they had been buried decently,' said Mr. Dibben sternly, 'there wouldn't be all this overcrowding.'

'Oh, there be room for woon more,' said Mr. Truggin.

The next week old Barker died.

A few days before he was forced to take to his bed, old Barker had shown a proper interest in the churchyard, which was highly pleasing to Mr. Truggin, who liked people to be glad to come there. 'For what be there to hurt 'ee,' he would say. 'An' for a half-crown extra I'd trim up thee's graveside as fine as a Christmas cracker, and who else be so safe an' well, or so well cared for as they happy dead!'

Old Barker had looked about him with the exact interest of one who is going to hire a new house. He noticed the birds. ' 'Tis all nice,' he said, looking about with approval, 'an' they little birds in yew tree be twittering.'

'All folk, birds and t'others, be happy here,' said Truggin, with the same superior gesture that the mayor of a town might give to a prospective builder of new and bright-coloured residential villas.

'Perhaps,' inquired Mr. Barker, in the mild voice of one who asks a favour, 'thee will let I in next to Aunt Jane; she did give I a penny when I were a young boy. . . .'

Mr. Truggin began to dig Barker's grave with all the satisfaction that a good workman shows when about his duties.

The idea of generous Aunt Jane pleased his imagination, but even if he had seen two bony fingers holding another penny, he wouldn't have touched it, because, of course, it was meant for her nephew Jimmy Barker, aged eighty.

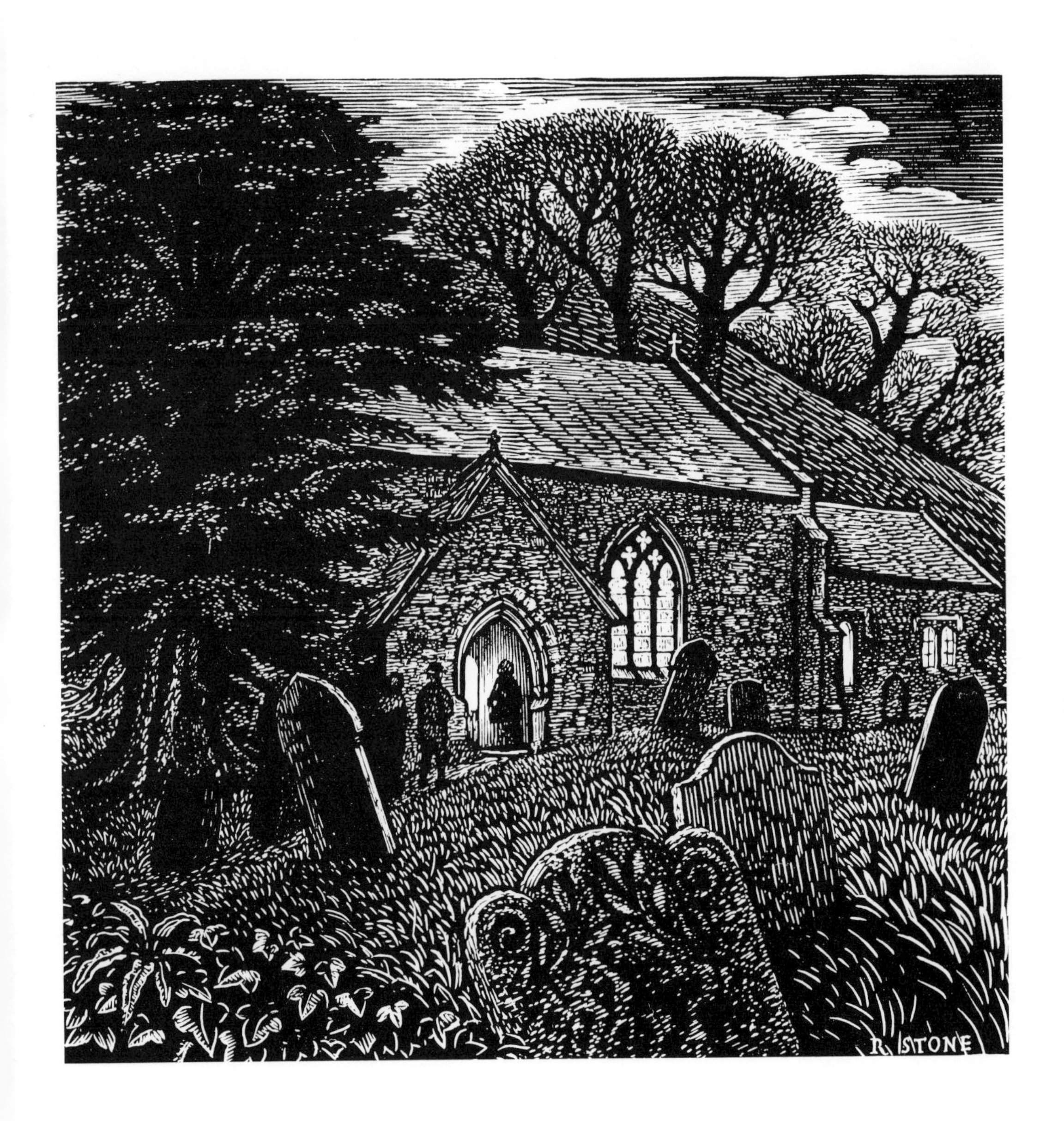
R. STONE

But when Mr. Dibben came to the churchyard and watched the proceedings, Mr. Truggin grew more and more nervous. Any others who had ever come to look had shown a proper and earthy interest, and a shudder at any dark stains that might be seen on the side of the grave, but Mr. Dibben watched from a different outlook altogether – a spiritual one.

The day was mild and it rained a little, and old Mr. Truggin, who kept his coat on as he worked, soon found himself unpleasantly warm.

Had he been alone he would never have done so foolish a thing as to take his coat off when he was hot and sweating; but what with Mr. Dibben watching him, and making unseemly remarks about the vileness of life and the glories of heaven – that were by no means the kind of subjects that Mr. Truggin were used to, or liked – Truggin clutched off his coat and cast it from him.

Mr. Dibben was beginning to speak in tones of exaltation about the grand awakening as Truggin carefully scraped the last shovelful of earth out of the grave. He patted the sides in a friendly manner.

'Wold Barker's bed be made,' he said, and climbed out of the grave.

When Mr. Truggin returned to his cottage he so far forgot himself as to say, ' 'T'won't do for they dead folk to hear no more of what parson do tell of, or they'll soon start a-swearing.'

'What did Mr. Dibben say?' inquired the sexton's lady.

'Nothing but insults to the dead,' replied Mr. Truggin. The sexton shivered.

'You bain't caught no cold, 'ave 'ee?' asked Mrs. Truggin.

'Most likely I have,' replied Mr. Truggin crossly. . . .

The spring winds gathered together that night, and shook the trees and threw to the ground many a little twig that was already decorated with spots of green. And splashes of rain driven through his roof by the gale fell upon Mr. Truggin, who lay ill.

' 'Tis a poor house, this be,' said the sexton, awaking about midnight from the heavy stupor that he had fallen into, and wiping the rain from his face. 'An' 'tis well I do know of a better.'

Mr. Truggin sat up in bed.

'Wold Barker bain't buried yet,' he said aloud, 'and Mr. Dibben do say there bain't no more room in Truggin's garden.'

The sexton looked at his wife; she slept soundly with her grey hair buried in the pillow.

Mr. Truggin smiled.

He crept from the bed and dressed slowly, shaking his head from side to side and smiling to himself as he put on each garment.

'A good dry housen where God Almighty be landlord and do keep roof in repair be best for I,' he muttered; 'an' 'tis right for Sexton Truggin to have the last house that be vacant.'

He softly closed the cottage door and went out into the night.

''Tain't stealing,' he said, 'and I'll tell wold Barker's aunt who I be.'

The church clock struck twelve. Dim clouds hurried quickly over the sky when Mr. Truggin reached the churchyard, and the moon peeped out between them as though to ask the dying sexton what he did there.

''Tis a pretty thing to see, a housen of woon's own making,' murmured Mr. Truggin, looking with pride at the open grave.

He stood for a moment to take a last look at the green mounds that he had tended for so long, and then, letting himself down into the grave, he lay contentedly at the bottom.

His stupor returned; he became unconscious. But after an hour or two he awoke and, turning his head a little, he remarked to the side of the grave:

'No, no, Aunt Jane, don't 'ee go handing I no money. I bain't thee's relation; I be Sexton Truggin.'

He remained contentedly conscious for the few moments that he was dying.

'No room,' he whispered, 'no more room.'

T. F. POWYS

INDEX OF TITLES

INDEX OF AUTHORS AND SOURCES

ACKNOWLEDGMENTS

Thanks are due to the following for permission to use:-

The stories *The Mighty Fallen, Negotiating From Weakness, Killed by Kindness, Bowing Before the Storm, A Philosophic Baldpate* and *Easily Remedied* from *Fables of Aesop* translated by S. A. Handford (Penguin Classics 1964 edition) © S. A. Handford 1954; the stories *The Fox and the Crow, The Human Being and the Dinosaur* and *The Unicorn in the Garden* from *Vintage Thurber* by James Thurber (The Collection Copyright © 1963 Hamish Hamilton Ltd. London); the stories *The Holy Man and the Snake* and *The Two Sons* from *Ramakrishna and His Disciples* by Christopher Isherwood and © The Vedanta Society of Southern California; the stories *King Banyan Deer* and *King Sivi* from *The Jataka Tales* adapted by E. B. Cowell published by Cambridge University Press; the stories *Ants, A Lovely Fist, A Man and His Pole, Like Man Like Monkey, Girls, The Thief, Competition in Weakness, Three Foolish Sisters, Father and Son, The Watch-Tower, Condolences, Who Farted?, A Mean Man* from *Oriental Humour* by R. H. Blyth published by the Hokuseido Press, Tokyo; the stories *The Woodcarver and the Peasants, Crocodile Tears, The Archer, A Very Short Sermon, Advice to A Man Who Was Concerned Over His Debts* from *Wit and Wisdom of the Italian Renaissance* by Charles Speroni (© 1964 by The Regents of the University of California) reprinted by permission of the University of California Press; for the stories *The Striker and the Stricken, The Grammarian and the Boatman, The Prescient Goldsmith, Omar and the Man who Thought He Saw the New Moon* from *Tales from the Masnavi* by A. J. Arberry published by George Allen & Unwin (Publishers) Ltd.; the stories *Worth, Time and Place, On His Own Funeral* from *Taoist Philosopher and Chinese Mystic* by H. A. Giles and Chuang-Tzu published by George Allen & Unwin (Publishers) Ltd.; the stories *Covetousness and Envy* by Jean Bodel and *The Man Who Had a Quarrelsome Wife* by Marie de France from *Fabliaux* by Robert Hellman and Richard F. O'Gorman published by Weidenfeld & Nicolson Ltd.; the stories *A Little Fable* and *A City Coat of Arms* from *Description of a Struggle and The Great Wall of China* by Franz Kafka published by Martin Secker and Warburg Ltd.; the story *Others Planted For Us* from *Persian Proverbs* by L. P. Elwell-Sutton published by John Murray (Publishers) Ltd.; the stories *The Dead Rat, The Servant and the Master, The Axe* from *Taoist Teachings: the Book of Lieh-Tzu* by L. Giles published by John Murray (Publishers) Ltd.; the story *The White Flag* from *A Dustbin of Milligan* by Spike Milligan published by Dennis Dobson Publishers; the story *The Bride* from *The White Paternoster* by T. F. Powys published by Chatto and Windus Ltd.; the story *The House with an Echo* from *The House with the Echo* by T. F. Powys published by Chatto and Windus Ltd.; the story *The Fool's Judgment* from *Rabelais* by John Cowper Powys published by The Village Press reprinted by kind permission of the Estate of the late John Cowper Powys; the story *The Talking Skull* from *African Genesis* by Leo Frobenius and Douglas C. Fox by permission of Stackpole Books.

The publishers would like to thank the following for permission to use the illustrations in this book:

London, Victoria & Albert Museum: 12 *Rackham,* 14, 15 *Boyd-Smith,* 17, 21, 22 *Boyd-Smith,* 23, 29, 34, 64, 77, 81. London, British Library: 13 *Condé,* 27, 30, 40, 52 *Jos. Hemard,* 54/55 *W. Heath Robinson,* 88/89 *Jos. Hemard,* 138 *W. Heath Robinson,* 144 *R. A. Garnett.* Dublin, Chester Beatty Library: 18. Boston, Museum of Fine Arts: 28 *Sesshu,* 73, 112. Vienna, Kunsthistorisches Museum/Snark: 39 *Brueghel.* Thurber: 47, 137. London, India Office Library: 74. Ch'en Hung-shou: 83. Cambridge, Fitzwilliam Museum: 91. Chao-yung: 92. San Francisco, M. H. De Young Memorial Museum: 93 *French School, c. 1500.* Spike Milligan: 104. Madrid, Prado Museum/ M. Holford: 111 *Brueghel.* Reynolds Stone: 153, 156. Bodleian Library: 43, 48, 50, 61, 79, 87, 99, 108, 117, 124, 129, 148 *E. R. Herman.*
Victoria & Albert Museum and British Library – photos Miki Slingsby.